The play of

JOHN STEINBECK'S THE PEARL

The play of
JOHN STEINBECK'S THE PEARL

by

Stuart Henson

HEINEMANN EDUCATIONAL BOOKS LTD
22 Bedford Square, London WC1B 3HH

LONDON EDINBURGH MELBOURNE AUCKLAND
SINGAPORE KUALA LUMPUR NEW DELHI IBADAN
NAIROBI JOHANNESBURG PORTSMOUTH (NH) KINGSTON

First published 1988

ISBN 435 23002 6

Photoset by Fakenham Photosetting Ltd, Fakenham, Norfolk
Printed in Great Britain by
J. W. Arrowsmith Ltd, Bristol and London

CONTENTS

Production notes

The setting

The setting of the play is flexible, and requires only two main locations. Most of the action takes place in Kino's brush house and on the shore nearby, whilst the climax of the play takes the characters into the desert mountains beyond Kino's village. The other locations, such as the Doctor's house and the Pearl Buyer's Office are represented by the use of the appropriate furniture and small spotlit areas.

In the original production, the brush house was built of light branches and walled with paper on two sides – a see-through construction, with a chimney at one end, which could be removed from the stage between Scenes 12 and 13. The floor of the stage suggests a sandy beach, with Kino's canoe drawn up near the house and perhaps a jetty with nets behind. The presence of the sea is suggested offstage opposite the house.

The mountains are represented by angular boulders and scrubby vegetation – free-standing scenery that may be moved to suggest a change of location between Scenes 14 and 15.

The music

The music provides not only the 'incidental' background, but is a voice in the drama itself. The principal themes, 'The Song of the Family', 'The Song of the Enemy' and 'The Song of the Pearl', reflect the states of mind of the characters. They are the songs which Kino hears at moments of crisis in the original story – they are part of Kino's apprehension of the world. In the play, they occur sometimes as a background to the dialogue itself, at others as links or bridges between scenes and choruses. The music has a Mexican or Central-American flavour; a music of the people, and of the natural world.

Main themes

'The Song of the Family': a haunting, tender melody; plain, harmonious, peaceful and pure.

'The Song of the Enemy': sinister, tense, threatening, but capable of being played quietly; a sense of seething evil.

'The Song of the Pearl': a richer melody than 'The Song of the Family'; it has an undersea quality, mysterious, yearning.

Incidental music

'The Music of Dawn' 'The Music of the Undersea' 'The Procession' 'The Music of Evil' 'A Lullaby' 'The Village Dance'

The themes from the original production are reprinted at the end of the play.

The role of the Chorus

The Choruses comment upon the action in the manner of the chorus in a Greek tragedy. In places, they also provide narrative links, and a sense of the passage of time. Some members of the chorus may well play lesser roles in the drama itself, and at several points the chorus of village people are actively involved in Kino and Juana's story. The choruses are written to be orchestrated among a number of voices, sometimes only two or three, sometimes ten or fifteen. Although there is little rhyme, it is intended that they should be spoken with the kind of attention to rhythm and sound that is given to poetry. Like the musicians, the chorus will be on or close to the stage area for the whole of the performance, so that their part may be integrated as easily as possible with the rest of the play.

In the original production, the chorus was split into two groups, working from either side of the stage. On some occasions, their voices were heard from the darkness; at other points the speakers moved on to stage, addressing the audience directly. In most cases, it proved more satisfactory to divide the lines for single voices rather than 'choral speaking', though Chorus 11 was spoken largely in unison, as were parts of a number of others. In both the vocal and visual presentation of the choruses the keynote is variety.

The dialogue

The dialogue follows the style of speech in the original story. Kino's people are economical with words, and in Steinbeck's writing their dignity is reflected in a slightly greater formality of language than we are familiar with in everyday conversation. Nevertheless, the actors should try to avoid a stilted or 'stage red-indian' delivery: it is the natural speech of a natural people.

Stuart Henson

THE PEARL

SYNOPSIS OF SCENES

Scene 1 *Kino's brush house. Morning.*
Scene 2 *The Doctor's house and at his gate.*
Scene 3 *The brush house. Morning.*
Scene 4 *Dance of the Undersea.*
Scene 5 *The beach and the brush house.*
Scene 6 *The brush house. Evening.*
Scene 7 *The brush house. Night.*
Scene 8 *The brush house and Kino's dream.*

Scene 9 *The brush house and the beach. Morning.*
Scene 10 *The Pearl Buyer's office.*
Scene 11 *The brush house. Evening.*
Scene 12 *The beach and the brush house. Night.*
Scene 13 *Juan Tomás' house.*
Scene 14 *Foothills of the mountains. Day.*
Scene 15 *The Mountains. Evening/night.*
Scene 16 *The beach; The Village Dance. Late afternoon/evening.*

THE PEARL

CHARACTERS

KINO a pearl fisherman
JUANA his wife
JUAN TOMÁS Kino's brother
APOLONIA Juan Tomás' wife
THE DOCTOR
THE DOCTOR'S WIFE
THE DOCTOR'S SERVANT
FIRST MERCHANT
SECOND MERCHANT
THIRD MERCHANT
PRIEST
COYOTITO (in Kino's dream)
FIRST BUYER
SECOND BUYER
THIRD BUYER
BUYER'S SERVANT
ROBBERS (3)
FIRST TRACKER
SECOND TRACKER
THIRD TRACKER

CHORUS: NEIGHBOURS, BEGGARS, PEOPLE OF KINO'S VILLAGE

THE PLAY OF THE PEARL

(*During the entrance of the audience, the* CHORUS OF VILLAGE PEOPLE *move freely on to and about the stage area: mending nets, preparing food, gossiping ... in short, just getting on with the day-to-day business of their lives (prepared improvisation). Some might barter and sell fruit or sweetmeats among the audience, tell fortunes etc. Then house and stage lights dim to darkness. 'The Music of Dawn' begins.*)

CHORUS 1

The sea whispers
first light
light on the water
whispers of dawn.
Thin light, and mist on the water,
sea whispers,
whispers of dawn.

All night the sea dreams
stories and whispers
driftwood and clusters
streams of green weed.
All night the sea dreams
of light on the water
mist on the water
whispers of dawn.

SCENE 1 *Kino's brush house. Morning.*

(Sound: birdsong, a distant dog barking, village noises suggesting dawn. Lights: a round red sun is rising very slowly on the backcloth. There is a low spotlight on KINO*'s house.* KINO *is asleep.* JUANA*, half-awake, is propped up on her elbows listening. A pause.* KINO *also wakes and watches.* JUANA *rises, almost ghostlike, and steps across to* COYOTITO*'s basket cradle hanging behind. She leans over, and reassures the baby, rocking the basket gently. Then she steps over the bedding and moves downstage a little to the fire-pit. She uncovers the coals and blows them alive as she breaks little pieces of brushwood over them. The firelight flickers. Music: 'The Song of the Family'.* JUANA *begins to grind flour with two stones. The rhythm becomes part of the music.* KINO *rises, moves to the door of the hut with his back towards* JUANA *as she works. He breathes the morning air and listens to the last notes of the music. There is a silence broken only by the sounds of birds and animals from the nearby huts, and by* JUANA *preparing the corn cakes.* KINO *turns back inside the hut.* JUANA *looks up.)*

JUANA: Will it be a good day, Kino?

KINO: I think it will. The sea will be a friend today. Maybe the sunshine will bring us good luck. Juan Tomás will go with me out beyond the edge of the reef, and we'll dive there. No-one has gone out there for a long time and we need to be lucky soon. Coyotito will need new clothes. When we have money we can go to the city. You shall have a new shawl, a new knife ... new combs and ribbons to put in your hair ...

(He reaches out to touch her hair but she is very serious, so he draws his hand back.)

JUANA: There is danger out beyond the reef. I am always afraid when you go there.

KINO: There is danger everywhere, even in the sheltered

water. Even in the grass by the huts there are snakes. On the roads there are thieves. But I am not afraid of dangers before they appear.

JUANA: A man cannot be full of fears, but a woman may still be afraid.

KINO: This morning the sun is shining: it will –

(*Suddenly* JUANA *lets out a little scream and clutches* KINO's *arm. She is staring in terror at the baby's cradle. What the couple can see is a black scorpion; it is working its way slowly down the rope that supports the cradle. [The presence of the scorpion might be suggested by using a shadow projection or a dummy scorpion suspended on cotton.]*)

JUANA: Kino! A scorpion!

(*Music: a percussion 'heartbeat' beginning quietly, building to a climax when* KINO *strikes at the scorpion and the baby screams.*)

KINO (*voice icy cold*): Be still, Juana.

(KINO *begins to creep stealthily towards the descending scorpion, every sinew in him tense, like a wild animal. Finally he leaps at the rope, the scorpion drops, and we hear the baby scream and begin to whimper.* KINO's *hands dive into the basket and he pulls out the scorpion, beating it into a pulp in his palm, and then crushing the remains into the ground with his heel and fist. His face is contorted with fear and anger.*

JUANA *runs to the basket and lifts out the bundle that represents the baby. Her first thought is to suck the poison out of the sting, spitting it away as she does so. Then she kneels beside* KINO, *rocking the baby with her whole body. She is half crying in terror, half soothing the baby. Music: the moaning sound* JUANA *makes, together with the percussion beat become the background to 'The Song of the Enemy'.*

During this pause, members of the CHORUS, *families from other huts, crowd around to see what the noise is about. Among them,* JUAN TOMÁS *and his family, who push their way through and into the doorway.*)

JUAN TOMÁS: What is it, Kino? What is it?

KINO: It is a scorpion, Juan Tomás. A scorpion has bitten Coyotito.

(JUAN TOMÁS *turns to* APOLONIA. *A murmur passes through the crowd.*)

CHORUS: A scorpion has bitten the baby.
The baby has been stung . . .

(APOLONIA *pushes across to* JUANA.)

APOLONIA: Let me see.

(JUANA *reluctantly gives up the 'baby', and* APOLONIA *examines the sting with an expert's interest.*)

APOLONIA: The wound is swelling already. It will depend on how much poison has gone in. (*She rocks the baby against her breast.*) Such a sting would be bad for you or me, but for a baby . . . a baby could die from the bite of a scorpion. (*Gravely*) In five hours we will know. The swelling comes first, then the fever, then the cramps in the stomach.

(JUANA *steps across and takes the baby from her. She is frightened, but in control of her emotions.*)

JUANA: The Doctor. We must ask for the Doctor.

(*A murmur of surprise passes into the crowd at the door.*)

JUAN TOMÁS: But the Doctor would not come here, Juana.

(The people at the door murmur their agreement.)

APOLONIA (*gently, as if talking to a child*): It has not been known. The Doctor will never come to a cluster of brush houses: he has more than he can do to care for the rich people who live in the town. The Doctor would not come here.

KINO (*resigned*): If we should send. He would not come.

(JUANA *turns on him with a kind of calm anger.*)

JUANA: Then we will go to him.

(The crowd reacts with a hushed awe. JUANA *passes the baby to* KINO *for a moment as she takes her shawl, arranging it over her head and into a sling to carry the baby and shade his eyes. As they prepare to go, the rumour spreads out among the rest of the* CHORUS.

CHORUS: They are going to the Doctor's house.
Kino and Juana are going to the Doctor's house (*etc.*).

(Music: 'The Song of the Family' transposed to a minor key.)

CHORUS 2

(As they leave the hut the people at the door push back to let KINO *and* JUANA *through. They are followed by* JUAN TOMÁS *and family; and the* VILLAGE PEOPLE, *excited and anxious, join on behind, making it a kind of animated procession. The procession may exit through the auditorium, and return that way, picking up chorus members as they go. Some may be beggars on the edge of the town. These too are anxious to see what will happen and join in. As the*

scene is set [downstage in a spotlight] for the DOCTOR's *house, the* CHORUS *speaks from the darkness of the auditorium.)*

NEIGHBOURS: By the sea the huts are built with brush
and the rooves are thatched with woven
leaves.

In the town the houses are plaster and stone.
At night there are lights and you cannot see
the stars.

By the sea the people drink from the springs.
They dance in the evening beside their
canoes.

In the town they dance to the gramophone.
Their water plays in cool fountains and drains
away.

By the sea the people are all poor.
In the town the beggars sit at the rich man's
gate.

BEGGARS: And we, the beggars, have seen the Doctor come
and go.
We have seen his carriage leave at ten.
We have seen men come to pay their bills.
We have seen his corpses pass to the Church.
We have seen his carriage return and the Doctor
drunk.

He has given us alms: the small brown pence that
weigh down his purse.
He has fed good meat to the dogs at his gate.
He has seen men starve.

He has sneered at me. He has driven the dust in my face.

NEIGHBOURS: What hope have these people who live by the sea
who rush to his house with their dying child,
with their simple fear and their ignorance,
and their need of help?

SCENE 2 *The Doctor's house and at his gate.*

(*The* DOCTOR'*s house and the* DOCTOR'*s gate. Two separate spots, lit alternately. In the* DOCTOR'*s chamber there is a bed or chaise-longue in which the* DOCTOR *is sitting up. He wears a silk dressing gown. On his lap are a silver tray with a silver chocolate pot and a tiny cup of delicate eggshell china, which looks ridiculous in his podgy hands. Beside him is a table with a small gong and a bowl of cigarettes. The* DOCTOR'S WIFE *is standing, somewhat aloof at the foot of the bed. There is clearly some tension between them.*)

DOCTOR: Well, it will have to stop. There is a limit. You have an allowance for clothes; you have an allowance for entertaining. I am quite prepared to spend a little more now and then. There are always unforeseen expenses, I realise that but –

DOCTOR'S WIFE: In my father's house –

DOCTOR: In your father's house there were thirty-five servants. In your father's house there were Persian rugs in every room. In your father's house, no doubt, the rats in the cellars had a pedigree. Unfortunately, though you may not have realised, you are no longer in your father's wonderful house. You are *my* wife and you are living in *my* house and you're going to have to learn to put up with it.

(*She responds with a sulky silence, turning away towards the door. He realises he has gone too far and begins to try to wheedle himself back into favour.*)

DOCTOR (*pouring himself another dainty cup of chocolate*): Very well, this time I will go and speak to the manager. I will arrange for credit. He owes me more than a favour, but it will be embarrassing.

DOCTOR'S WIFE (*turning back to him*): And it's not embarrassing for me, I suppose, when I have to apologise for being late because I have to hire a public carriage? And it's not embarrassing when I have to wear the same dresses time after time and hear the other women talking behind my back?

DOCTOR: You must understand that it's not what I wish. Very soon we shall move to a bigger place. Perhaps one day we shall go back to France. In this town there are too many people who want to talk, and too few who are prepared to pay for a doctor's skills. My list has got smaller by the year. The natives are moving into the towns and the best sort of people are moving north. There are whole suburbs of stinking little huts going up between the railway and the river. They live like animals: it would be a better place for a veterinary than a doctor . . .

CHORUS 3

(*As the crowd arrives at the* DOCTOR'*s gate, we hear the voices of the* CHORUS *echo.*)

What hope have these people who live by the sea
who rush to this house with their crying child?

What hope when they reach these places of cruel
high walls and cool gardens hidden away from the road
where the fountains play and the jasmine flowers,
and the brick-red bougainvillea grows?

(*The crowd gathers a few steps behind* KINO *and* JUANA. *There is an expectant silence.* KINO *hesitates, as if he is unsure of what to do.*)

JUAN TOMÁS: You must ring the bell, Kino.

(KINO *tugs at the bell pull suspiciously. On the other side of the stage, behind the* DOCTOR's *house, the bell rings.* KINO *looks around at the crowd. There is another silence and a long pause.*)

JUANA (*firmly*): Ring it again.

(KINO *does so. Immediately we hear the voice of the* DOCTOR's SERVANT.)

SERVANT: One moment! One moment! Patience!

(*The gate opens a few inches and the* SERVANT *looks out suspiciously.*)

SERVANT: What do you want, you people?
KINO: The little one – the first-born – has been poisoned by a scorpion. He requires the skill of the healer.
SERVANT: This will not be possible, I think.

(*He shuts the gate, but* KINO *bangs on it with his fist. The gate opens a few inches again.*)

KINO: The child is very sick. He may die soon if we cannot have the Doctor's help.

(*He forces his foot into the gap. The* SERVANT, *looking down, realises he cannot shut the gate.*)

SERVANT (*sulkily*): Very well, a little moment. I shall go to inform him myself.

(KINO *releases the gate, which the* SERVANT *immediately shuts and bolts.* KINO *turns back to the others.*)

JUAN TOMÁS: This man, this servant. He lived in the brush huts once. He was a fisherman.

(*The spotlights change again, returning us to the house. The* SERVANT *enters and waits at the open doorway to be noticed.*)

DOCTOR: Yes? What is it?

SERVANT: Patron, it is a little Indian with a baby. He says a scorpion stung it.

DOCTOR (*pausing to put down his cup; with a sneer*): Have I nothing better to do than cure insect bites for 'little Indians'?

SERVANT: Yes, Patron.

DOCTOR: Has he any money? (*Silence*) No, they never have any money. I, I alone in the world am supposed to work for nothing – and I'm tired of it. See if he has any money.

(*The* SERVANT *turns rapidly and exits.*)

DOCTOR'S WIFE: Perhaps this time, just this once, you could see the child. It's probably nothing. You know how the Indians panic. You could just give them something to take away the inflammation . . .

DOCTOR: You don't learn, do you? Isn't it obvious what will happen if I treat this one? By six o'clock there will be a whole queue of them waiting at the gate – all expecting me to cure their little illnesses for nothing.

(*The* SERVANT *arrives at the gate and unbolts it, as before.*)

SERVANT: I must ask if you have any money to pay for the treatment?

KINO (*looking at* JUANA, *then reaching into his clothing*): My friend, I have no money at present. But I can pay the Doctor with these.

(*He holds out a creased and folded paper which the* SERVANT *opens. The* SERVANT *looks doubtfully at the pearls inside and at* KINO.)

SERVANT: One minute, please.

(*He scurries back to the* DOCTOR'*s room.*)

SERVANT: Patron, the Indian has no money, but he has pearls. Here –

(*The* SERVANT *takes the packet across to the bedside and opens it.*)

DOCTOR: Bah! These are nothing. They are only little seed pearls, and ugly as ulcers. They are quite flat – and valueless. Take them back.

(*The* SERVANT *hurries off again.*)

DOCTOR'S WIFE: Why not take them? You could give them to me.

DOCTOR: My darling, you wouldn't be seen dead with such things. If it is pearls you want, I know a dealer. You can choose what you like, as long as it's within reason . . .

(*The* SERVANT *arrives back at the gate. He unbolts it as before.*)

SERVANT (*coldly*): The doctor has gone out. He was called away to a serious case.

(*He shuts the gate quickly, out of shame. The crowd begins to melt away leaving* KINO *and* JUANA *alone at the gate. At last* KINO *puts his hat back on his head. They turn away. Then* KINO *suddenly spins round and with an inarticulate cry of frustration and anger he smashes his fist against the gate.*)

CHORUS 4

So we must melt away,
and become shadows;
we who came to watch;
we who have seen what we hoped
we should not see.

We are all ashamed:
we have seen too much;
we have seen what we knew
in our hearts we would see.

And now we must share
in the shame of a man
who has gone to a place
where he knows he may be refused
and is turned away.

We are ashamed . . .
　　　　　　We are ashamed . . .
and like shadows
　　　　　　we melt away.

(*Music: to cover the scene break and to suggest the passage of time. Themes from the 'Dawn Music' or 'The Song of the Family'.*)

SCENE 3 *The brush house. Morning.*

(KINO *is sharpening his knife.* JUANA *is tending the fire. There is a silence between them.*)

JUANA: He is not crying so often, now.

(KINO *stops sharpening his knife. He shrugs his shoulders.* JUANA *crosses to him.*)

Scene 3 The brush house. Morning

JUANA: The gods may hear our prayers, Kino.

(KINO *does not respond.*)

JUANA: I have prayed to the Mother Mary, also. (*She pauses*) I prayed that today you will find a pearl, a good pearl, big enough to hire the Doctor. Coyotito is strong. He is no worse this morning. If we could persuade the Doctor – I'm sure he would get well.

(KINO *looks into her eyes, then at the cradle. It is as if he wishes to say something, but cannot find the words. Then they both look towards the door as* APOLONIA *bustles in.*)

APOLONIA (*going directly to the basket cradle*): The child is not dead. Praise be to Jesus!

JUANA: His face is feverish. His neck and his ear are swollen and hot.

APOLONIA: Has he had the cramps in the stomach yet?

JUANA: No, Apolonia, there were no cramps. I think perhaps I was able to suck away the worst of the poison.

(JUANA *crosses to the cradle and reaches in gently.*)

JUANA: I have made a seaweed poultice. This is my mother's medicine for snake bites and stings.

APOLONIA: The old medicines were good, but they are not like the Doctor's.

(KINO *has gathered up his diving-ropes and basket and fixed his knife in his belt. He steps to the door and turns.*)

KINO: I must be gone now. In two hours, maybe three, we shall be back.

(JUANA *watches him from the doorway. The lights fade on the hut. Outside, we see* KINO *drag his canoe down to the water's edge.*)

CHORUS 5

Kino . . .
          Kino . . .
                    Kino . . .
                              Kino . . .
The sea whispers;
all day the sea whispers,
whispers its mysteries
whispers its songs.

All day the sea calls,
its voices of azure and emerald
voices of shells
                    voices of shells
and the hush
of the great roll
of the deeps.

Somewhere . . .
          Somewhere . . .
                    Somewhere . . .
                              Somewhere . . .
the Song of the Undersea.

Somewhere . . .
          Somewhere . . .
                    Somewhere . . .
                              Somewhere . . .
the Song of the Pearl that might be . . .

(Music: 'The Song of the Pearl'/ 'The Music of the Undersea'.)

SCENE 4 *Dance of the Undersea.*

(As the music takes over, a separate area downstage fades up in deep blues and greens. The effect should be one of rippling and moving to

suggest depth of water. During the dance, strobe or ultra-violet light might be used to heighten the mysterious slow-motion effect. Then a dance/movement sequence, possibly using members of the CHORUS, *begins in very slow-motion with controlled and stylised movements. The dancers may carry – singly or between them – materials suggesting plant shapes, fish, shoals, oysters . . ., foil textures reflecting the light and weed textures. The dancers may wear masks to cover their faces. They move in and out of the lit area, which need not be very big. Some may blow children's soap bubbles, possibly sitting, rock-like, with their backs to the audience. The visual effect should be rather like watching the undersea life in the beam of an underwater camera.*

As part of the dance, KINO *moves among the plants and fishes. He gathers oysters into his basket which is attached to a rope suspended from above. All his movements are slowed by the water as he 'swings' from oyster to oyster. Finally his movement takes him to the largest oyster which will contain the Pearl.* KINO *places the giant oyster into his basket and looks up, perhaps pulling on the rope. As his legs push up from the floor, the undersea lights fade quickly, the movements of his hands and arms suggesting that he is about to swim up to the surface.)*

SCENE 5 *The beach and the brush house.*

(Lights rise on the upstage 'beach' area outside the hut. KINO *is drawing up the canoe. He snatches out his basket in great excitement.* JUANA *looks up expectantly as he enters the hut.* KINO *says nothing, but puts down the basket and coils his rope from his shoulder. He is pretending not to be anxious to open the oysters.)*

KINO (*after a pause*): How is the child now?

JUANA: I think he is going to be well. When I took away the seaweed, the swelling had gone down. I think the poison is going from his body.

KINO (*hinting at something*): Perhaps luck is with us today.
JUANA: You have opened the oysters?
KINO: Not yet. (*Pause*) Sometimes you think you see a glint before the shell closes.
JUANA: I have prayed, Kino. (*Softly*) Open them. Now.

(KINO *takes his knife and slits open an oyster from the basket. It is empty.* JUANA *looks up at his face. He opens another and again it is empty.* JUANA *puts her hand on* KINO*'s arm as he reaches into the basket again.*)

JUANA: The big one, Kino. Open the biggest one.

(*He is almost trembling as he takes the biggest oyster and cuts into the gap in the shell. Music: 'The Song of the Pearl'. As* KINO *pulls open the top half of the shell and lifts the flesh away,* JUANA *gasps. Slowly,* KINO *lifts a great translucent pearl high in his hand. It is almost the size of a bantam's egg.* KINO *looks at the cradle and then at* JUANA*, then he clenches his fists and puts back his head and howls with joy. The lights fade quickly, leaving his cry echoing with the last strains of 'The Song of the Pearl'.*)

CHORUS 6

(*Out of the darkness and the silence following* KINO*'s howl, a seething whisper begins. At first it is quite unintelligible, but then, as it moves across the stage area, it becomes clear what the members of the* CHORUS *are saying.*)

CHORUS: Kino has found the Pearl of the World.
Kino has found a great white pearl.
Kino has found the greatest pearl in the world.
The fisherman Kino has struck it rich –
Kino has found a pearl as big as a gull's egg. (*etc.*)

Chorus 6

(The whisper passes in a chain among the CHORUS *– possibly into the auditorium. The* BEGGARS, *the* DOCTOR, *the* PEARL DEALERS *and the* PRIEST, *move briefly through, or are picked out by, spotlights as they are caught hearing the news and thinking aloud.)*

BEGGARS: Kino has found the Pearl of the World.
We must rattle our tins.
We must bring our sickly children.
There is no alms giver in the world
like a poor man who is suddenly lucky.

SERVANT: Patron, they are saying that Kino has been lucky: he has found a great pearl, the Pearl of the World.
DOCTOR: Kino? Who is this Kino?
SERVANT: You remember, Patron, the little Indian at the gate?
DOCTOR: Ah, the Indian, Kino. He is a client of mine, I am treating his child for a scorpion sting.

DEALERS: They say an Indian has found a gigantic pearl.
The people call it the Pearl of the World.
He must bring this pearl to us.
We are the only dealers in this town.
This pearl will be the making of us.

PRIEST: Kino has found a beautiful pearl? This Kino perhaps is among the Indians who stand at the back of the church. Perhaps it is God's will I should visit him. If he is a good Christian, there are many repairs he may do for the Church . . .

(The CHORUS *ends with the whisper reaching a crescendo in which the voices speak in unison.)*

CHORUS: Kino has found the Pearl of the World!

(Music: 'The Song of the Pearl'/'The Song of the Family'.)

SCENE 6 *The brush house. Evening.*

(*Lights rise on the house. Evening.* KINO *and* JUANA *are seated centre,* KINO *holding the pearl in his hands,* JUANA *rocking the baby cradled in her shawl. On* KINO*'s right is* JUAN TOMÁS. APOLONIA *is on* JUANA*'s left. Their family and a crowd of* NEIGHBOURS *are looking on. The music continues softly through the opening dialogue.*)

JUAN TOMÁS (*laughing*): And what will you do, now you are a rich man?

KINO (*far away in his imagination*): Ah!

(KINO *pauses. He looks at* JUANA.)

KINO: Now we can afford it – we will be married, in the Church.

(JUANA *casts her eyes down, afraid her excitement will show.*)

KINO: I can see it here in the pearl. Juana is wearing a shawl that is so new the patterns dance in your eyes, and a fine skirt . . . and shoes . . .

APOLONIA: And you, Kino; you are dressed in new white clothes, and a new hat –

JUAN TOMÁS: Not a straw hat, but fine black felt! And no sandals for the wedding, but shoes that lace –

APOLONIA: And little Coyotito, he'll be the one! He must have a blue sailor suit from the United States. And Juan Tomás and me and the children, we must have new clothes –

KINO: I can get a new harpoon – of iron, with a ring in the end of the shaft, so it cannot be lost like the old one. (*His mind begins to leap*) And a rifle. Kino shall have a rifle!

JUAN TOMÁS: Or a Winchester Carbine!

(JUAN TOMÁS *strikes a pose with the imaginary gun and the* NEIGHBOURS *join in the excitement.*)

NEIGHBOURS (*whispering*): A rifle. Kino will buy himself a rifle!

KINO (*rising to his feet, transported by his imagination*): Coyotito shall go to school. I have seen it through the doorway. Coyotito shall sit at a desk. He will write on great white sheets of paper. He shall have the uniform of the school-children. (*Fiercely now, as he looks around at his* NEIGHBOURS) My son will read and open the books. My son will write and will know writing. And my son will make numbers, and these things will make us free because he will know – he will know, and through him we will know. (*Almost shouting*) Coyotito shall sit here, and read to us all, from a great book! This is what the pearl will do!

(*Suddenly, with* KINO*'s shout, there is an eerie silence.* KINO *closes his hand over the pearl. The light has dimmed a little during this speech.* JUANA *moves to attend to the fire, and the flames begin to dance. One or two* NEIGHBOURS, *nodding a goodbye to* KINO, *drift away to their own houses. They mime animated conversation as they go together, lifting their hands and shaking their heads. One of the* NEIGHBOURS *notices the* PRIEST, *and a whisper passes in to* KINO.)

NEIGHBOURS: The father is coming – the priest is coming.

(*The* MEN *uncover their heads and step back from the door; the* WOMEN *gather their shawls about their faces and cast down their eyes.* KINO *and* JUAN TOMÁS *stand up. The* PRIEST *nods and raises his hand in greeting to the people he passes. He is an ageing figure, but sharp-eyed. He has a somewhat patronising manner of smiling and nodding as he speaks.*)

PRIEST: My children. (*A pause and a sigh*) Ah, Kino. Thou art named after a great man – and a great father of the Church. Thy namesake was one who tamed the desert and sweetened the minds of thy people. Did'st thou know that? It is written in the chronicles of our nation.

(*Music: very faintly, a few bars from 'The Song of the Enemy'.*)

PRIEST: It has come to me that thou hast found a great fortune, a great pearl.

(KINO *opens his hand and holds out the pearl. The* PRIEST *almost gasps aloud at its size and beauty.*)

PRIEST: I hope thou wilt remember to give thanks, my son, to Him who has given thee this treasure – and to pray for guidance in the future.

(KINO *looks down.*)

JUANA (*softly*): We shall, Father. And we will be married now. Kino has said so.

(*She looks round at the* NEIGHBOURS *and they nod their assent.*)

PRIEST: It is pleasant to see that your first thoughts are good thoughts. The Devil sets many traps for the innocent. Perhaps we shall see thee in the church on Sunday?

(KINO *nods dumbly. The* PRIEST *looks round significantly.*)

PRIEST: Remember the Sabbath Day, and keep it holy. Even those who cannot read may know the Commandments. (*To* KINO) You will take your pearl to sell in the town before the week is out?

KINO: We will.

PRIEST (*simpering*): Well, may God bless thy endeavours.

Perhaps it is decreed thou shalt become a wealthy man. But then must thou beware, and be sure thou givest to thy Mother Church in full measure, for the Scripture saith it is easier for a camel to go through the eye of a needle than for a rich man to enter the kingdom of God.

(*The people murmur and the* PRIEST *turns and goes to the door. He stops and turns for a dramatic effect.*)

PRIEST: Take care thy soul is not corrupted by Mammon, for the Lord is a jealous God and will punish them that worship the things of the earth.

(*With this he makes his exit. The people whisper.*)

NEIGHBOUR: If it were my pearl, I should give it as a present to the Holy Father in Rome.

(*The others grunt or murmur in response.*)

NEIGHBOUR'S WIFE: It would buy Masses for the souls of our families for a thousand years.

(*These two and the remaining* NEIGHBOURS *nod their goodnights and slip away into the encroaching darkness beyond the house.* KINO *is left clutching the pearl tightly in his fist.* JUANA *takes the baby and gently puts him into his cradle. Then, while* JUANA *sets a cooking pot over the flames of the fire,* KINO *goes to the door and looks out at the night. He is thinking, resolving things in his mind. Music: 'The Song of the Family' – perhaps on a solo instrument – drifts very quietly in and out for a few bars.*)

SCENE 7 *The brush house. Night.*

(*The* SERVANT *and the* DOCTOR *approach. The* SERVANT *is carrying a lantern and the* DOCTOR*'s bag.* KINO *becomes alert and* *tense. The* SERVANT *raises the lantern to light their faces, but* KINO *utters no word of greeting.)*

DOCTOR: I was not in when you came this morning. But now at the first chance, I have come to see the baby.
KINO (*blocking the doorway*): The baby is nearly well now.
DOCTOR (*after a slight pause*): Ah! Sometimes, my friend, the scorpion sting has a curious effect. There will be apparent improvement, and then without warning . . .

(*He purses his lips and makes a sound like a flame popping out.* KINO *looks doubtfully into his face. The* DOCTOR *deliberately takes his bag from the* SERVANT, *holding it so that the light falls on it.*)

DOCTOR: Sometimes, sometimes there will be a withered leg or a blind eye or a crumpled back. Oh, I know the sting of the scorpion, my friend, and I can cure it.

(*After a long and thoughtful pause,* KINO *steps aside and the* DOCTOR *and the* SERVANT *enter.* JUANA *instinctively moves to stand between the* DOCTOR *and the cradle.*)

DOCTOR: I have come to see the child.

(JUANA *looks at* KINO. KINO *nods. Reluctantly* JUANA *lifts the baby out. The* DOCTOR *reaches out to take the baby. Again* JUANA *hesitates before she steps forward and gives* COYOTITO *to him.*)

DOCTOR (*to the servant*): Hold the lantern!

(*He examines the wound on the baby's shoulder with his back to the audience. There is possibly a sound of crying.*)

DOCTOR: It is as I thought. The poison has gone inwards and it will strike soon. (*To* KINO) Come, look!

(KINO *steps closer.*)

DOCTOR: See how the eyelid is blue: a sure sign.

(KINO *frowns. The* DOCTOR *looks into his eyes and speaks with a feigned emotion.*)

DOCTOR: I will give him something to try to turn the poison aside. I cannot guarantee. But I will do my best.

(*The* DOCTOR *hands the baby to* KINO *and then turns to work, briskly and efficiently. He takes a little bottle of white powder and a capsule of gelatine from his bag, fills the capsule with powder and closes it. Then he takes the baby from* KINO *and, holding* COYOTITO *in his left hand, appears to make the baby swallow the capsule which he has in his right. [Again, having his back to the audience may help the illusion.] There is a sound of crying. He reaches down for a pitcher on the floor and gives the baby a drink. He looks carefully at the baby's face as he turns back and seems to be deep in thought. He purses his lips. He hands the baby to* JUANA *and turns to* KINO.)

DOCTOR: I think the poison will attack within the hour. But the medicine may save the baby from hurt. I will come back in an hour. Perhaps I am in time to save him.

(*He takes a deep breath and exits, followed by his* SERVANT *with the bag and the lantern.* KINO *stands at the door watching them go. Music: 'The Song of the Pearl', quietly.* KINO *moves back into the centre of the hut. He holds up the pearl and examines it in the firelight.* JUANA *watches him in silence. Then he takes the scarf from his neck and wraps the pearl in it. He moves to the corner of the brush house, digs a little hole in the earth floor and conceals the pearl there. He returns to* JUANA. *She is looking at the baby's face.*)

KINO: Is it blue, under the eyelid, as the doctor said?
JUANA: I think so. It's hard to tell.
KINO: I cannot trust that man; yet I must trust him. (*A pause, then suddenly, beating his fist on the floor*) But *how* can I know!

CHORUS 7

There are many things a man may not know.
He may not know what the day will bring:
sorrow, laughter, fortune, anger . . .
these things are hidden,
beyond the knowledge of men.

There are many things a man may not know.
He may not know what lies in the heart
of the stranger who comes to his gate,
or what truth there is in the books
that he has not read.

He may not know if the sick child
will grow strong again, or its limbs wither
and stunt like a vine without rain.
He must trust the man who has read
where these secrets are.

But his eyes burn
and his soul is clenched with pain.

(*Music: a few bars of 'The Song of the Enemy', drifting.*)

SCENE 8 *The brush house and Kino's dream.*

(*The sound of rustling, jingling and voices from the darkness.* KINO*'s hand goes to the knife in his belt. He turns to* JUANA.)

KINO: Someone is out there.

(JUANA *puts the baby quickly, but carefully, down in his cradle. They wait together in silence, watching through the doorway. The* MERCHANTS *arrive in a group, one of them whistling. They bring caged birds, rolled rugs and a wooden samples box. The style of their dress is brash, almost gaudy; their manner noisy, jovial, 'foot-in-the-door'. It is as if they are almost, but not quite, drunk. Their patter is ingratiating and well-practised. They make a sinister trio.*)

1ST MERCHANT: A good night to you, Kino!
KINO: I know these men. They are from the marketplace in La Paz.
2ND MERCHANT: You must forgive us for calling on you so late, but we have been in the market all day. We have heard of your great fortune. We come to bring our good wishes.
3RD MERCHANT: Our congratulations. We wanted to be the first. May we come in?
KINO (*eyeing them with suspicion*): I have no use for your cheap goods. (*A slight hesitation, then aggressively*) I have found the Pearl of the World.
1ST MERCHANT: Indeed. From now on it is Kino the Rich Man.
2ND MERCHANT: In the marketplace they will say no longer, 'Here comes Kino the fisherman.' They will say, 'Put on a smart appearance: it is a *gentleman*!
3RD MERCHANT (*pushing past* KINO *into the hut*): You will not wish to stay here among the huts when you have sold your pearl. You will buy a house. A fine white house, on a shady street.

(*The other two follow him in.*)

2ND MERCHANT: A house with many rooms, a garden – and servants.

1ST MERCHANT: In the afternoon you will rest in the cool of the house. You will send your servant out to the marketplace. A rich man has need of many things. See, we have brought you the very best there is to be had.

2ND MERCHANT (*deftly unrolling one of the rugs*): No longer will you walk on floors of sand. Even now, here in this hut, you can walk on soft rugs. This one you will see is extremely beautiful. It is this pattern I sell to the Doctor; also Ramon the Government Clerk has purchased one – and Don Carlos the big boss at the hacienda, he has three in his great bedrooms. Please – walk. You will feel how soft the pile is on your toes . . .

KINO: I have no need of such things. Yet.

2ND MERCHANT: In the cities such a rug would not be bought for fifty American dollars. But here, because you are my friend, two hundred pesos –

KINO: In this house, such a rug would spoil. We have everything that is necessary.

2ND MERCHANT: Ah! I can see that you will drive hard bargains in the marketplace. This is good, for a *gentleman*. But I am your friend: so today I will leave you this rug for fifty pesos only. And when you have sold your pearl . . .

JUANA: A fisherman does not keep such money. You must wait. There is a saying: 'Before tomorrow there are many days.'

1ST MERCHANT: There is also a saying: 'Bite the cherry when it's ripe.' Fortune has smiled on your house. It is a lucky house, and such a house should be filled with laughter, and birdsong.

(*He slips off the cloth from one of the cages.*)

1ST MERCHANT: You see, a beauty, and the cage would hang so prettily, here from the rafter. (*Ingratiatingly to* JUANA) And the baby, it will watch the bird, and hear it sing, and it will laugh too – it will grow up happy.

(*There is no response from* JUANA, *so he continues.*)

1ST MERCHANT: This one I will give you – for the baby. A present. Only the cage I cannot give. That is twenty-five pesos in the town.

(*There is still no response from* JUANA, *so he turns to* KINO.)

1ST MERCHANT: It is a good bird, a cock bird. The hen is not so bright, and she does not sing like him. I shall be sorry to lose him. They are not so easy to get. Anyone can catch you a hen-bird. We put out the cage traps, and because he is proud, even in his cage the male will sing, and the female – ah, they are so simple – she will come down to his call; she will even walk into a cage if the male is there, and then . . .

(*He makes a gesture to show the cage door springing shut and laughs.*)

1ST MERCHANT: But this is a cock bird, and the cage is good –

(JUANA *steps forward and takes the cage from his hand.*)

JUANA: For the baby?
1ST MERCHANT: I have said. And the cage is not expensive.

(JUANA *runs out into the darkness beyond the hut.*)

1ST MERCHANT (*shouting after her*): In the big houses they have cages like this hanging on the verandas . . .

(*The* 3RD MERCHANT *opens his box like a conjurer as he moves close to* KINO.)

3RD MERCHANT: But for a gentleman, he must go out into the world. He must do business in the clubs and the great buildings. It is not for him to be standing on the idle street in the sun. For this he must keep to the times he has set for his trade. He will glance at his watch on a silver chain.

(*He draws up a pocket watch in front of* KINO's *eyes.*)

3RD MERCHANT: He will say, 'In one hour I shall speak with the *Captain* of my ship. At midday the *Judge* will call at my house and we shall drink coffee together ...' I am very fortunate. This watch I am able to buy from a friend who has brought them across the border without paying tax. There are not many fishermen who could afford such a fine piece. But I can tell that you are a man who is not fooled by everything that glitters in the light: you can tell when such a thing is worth five hundred pesos –

KINO (*pushing the box to the floor in anger*): Enough! Go! (*Then quietly, when the merchant has scrabbled to pick up his goods*) Each day of my life I have watched the sun rise by the hills of the eastern shore; I have watched it sink like an old fire in the western sea. My shadow walks with me along the beach. I have no need of your trash. Be gone!

3RD MERCHANT (*bitterly*): You are a proud man, Kino. Beware, Your pride will make you many enemies.

KINO: This is my house. I did not ask you in.

(*The* MERCHANTS *are gathering their things and are just about to exit when* JUANA *returns with the cage, but the cage door is open and the bird gone.*)

1ST MERCHANT: But where is the bird?

JUANA: It has flown away – to the moon.

1ST MERCHANT: You are a foolish woman; you will not catch such a bird again in these parts. That is twenty-five pesos you have let fly away!

JUANA: And where should I get twenty-five pesos?

1ST MERCHANT: You should have thought about that before

you let it go. I have sold it; you have bought it. It is not my problem if you wish to keep an empty cage. Maybe I can get you another bird, but at this time of year, it could be more expensive . . .

JUANA (*thrusting the cage at him*): But it is not our cage. I had no wish to buy a cage. Only the bird was Coyotito's. That is what you said. And he shall hear him singing in the dawn on the tree by the roof. He will sing for Coyotito, who has given him back his freedom. Now, go. My husband has no wish to trade with anyone tonight.

(*The* MERCHANTS *spit curses and grumble one to another, but they know they are beaten, and they exit the way they came, their mutterings disappearing into the night.*)

JUANA: Last night we were alone. These people are vultures. (*After a pause, with real urgency in her voice*) Kino, I am afraid of what this pearl will do!

KINO (*frustration and anger getting the better of him*): Woman!

(*He turns away from her moodily. There is a long silence between them.* KINO *picks up a piece of wood and begins to hack at it with a knife. Suddenly the baby's cry is heard again.* JUANA *rushes to the cradle. The crying is frantic.*)

JUANA: Kino! He is sick! He's choking, Kino!

(*She lifts the baby out and cradles him in her shawl, anxiously. She kneels in the firelight to examine the baby's face.* KINO *kneels beside her, the tension between them forgotten.*)

KINO: So the Doctor knew!

(*The baby's crying continues.* JUANA *croons a lullaby – the melody of 'The Song of the Family' – rocking back and forward on her knees in desperation.* KINO *runs to the door of the hut and shouts into the darkness.*)

KINO: Juan Tomás! Juan Tomás! The baby is dying! Juan Tomás!

(KINO *rushes back to* JUANA'*s side, his arm round her shoulders, half clutching the baby himself.* JUAN TOMÁS *appears, half-undressed in the doorway.*)

KINO: You must fetch the Doctor again! The baby is very sick! Go quickly! Please!

(JUANA *continues to croon. The baby continues to cry. 'The Music of Evil' beats in the background.* APOLONIA *comes running towards them in a state of excitement. Other* NEIGHBOURS *from the Chorus crowd around. The whisper runs out, repeated urgently in the darkness around the auditorium.*)

NEIGHBOURS: Fetch the Doctor. Go quickly. The baby is very sick.
Fetch the Doctor. Go quickly. Please . . .

(*Some of the* WOMEN *squat down by* JUANA *and* KINO. *Amid the other noises, they may be heard giving advice.*)

WOMEN: Loosen his wrap.
Don't hold the child on its back.
Get something cold for his forehead.
You must keep his temperature down.
Will he drink some water?
All things are in God's hands. (*etc.*)

(*Then suddenly, as the confusion reaches its height, the* DOCTOR *appears, with his* SERVANT, *roughly brushing away the gathered* WOMEN. *He takes the baby immediately from* JUANA *and holds it up momentarily. Apart from the crying, there is a sudden silence. The* DOCTOR *has made the perfect dramatic entrance. Now he begins to capitalise on the effect.*)

DOCTOR: The poison of the scorpion is working now. (*Pause*) But I think I can defeat it. I will try my best.

(*He examines the baby's throat and places his hand across its forehead. He turns to* JUANA.)

DOCTOR: Water!

(JUANA *brings him a cup and a little pitcher of water. Whilst she does so, the* DOCTOR *places the baby in the cradle. He takes off his coat, which the* SERVANT *holds, and rolls up his sleeves. From his bag he takes a bottle and a medicine glass. He takes the pitcher roughly from* JUANA *and pours a little water into the glass. Then he mixes three drops from the bottle and the liquid clouds. He holds it up to the light.*)

DOCTOR: It is lucky that I know the poison of the scorpion, otherwise –

(*He shrugs his shoulders to indicate what could have happened. He turns back to the cradle and the* WOMEN *gather closer as he administers the mixture. The baby's cries redouble.* JUANA *crosses herself and kneels in fervent prayer.* APOLONIA *tries to comfort her.*)

APOLONIA: We are all in God's hands. You are young and strong. There can be more children.

(*The crying continues. The* NEIGHBOURS *look knowingly at one another. One or two shake their heads. As if by a silent command, they go out.* KINO *just stares darkly at the* DOCTOR's *bag. An* OLDER NEIGHBOUR *embraces him in a gesture of sympathy as he passes. Only* JUAN TOMÁS *and* APOLONIA *remain. The* SERVANT, *still holding the coat, smiles weakly, but the others simply ignore him. The* DOCTOR *turns from the cradle and buttons down his sleeves. The baby's crying is becoming more intermittent. The* DOCTOR *beckons* JUANA *to the cradle.*)

DOCTOR: Don't worry. He will get well. He will sleep soon. I have won the fight.

(JUANA *clasps his hand suddenly and falls again to her knees at his feet. The* DOCTOR *is embarrassed.* KINO *looks away downstage. The* DOCTOR *lifts his hand away gently and motions to the* SERVANT *for his coat. The* SERVANT *then begins to pack up his bag.*)

DOCTOR: It is not a great thing. The wisdom of men is greater than the poison of the scorpion. (*He steps downstage to* KINO, *speaking almost kindly*) There will be, of course, the small matter of my bill. Do you think you will be able to pay it –

KINO (*turning to look at him directly*): When I have sold my pearl, I will pay you.

DOCTOR (*feigning surprise and interest*): You have a pearl? A good pearl?

JUAN TOMÁS (*breaking in*): Kino has found the Pearl of the World! As big as this. And white as the dawn.

APOLONIA: Kino will be a rich man in the morning. Such a pearl has never been found in these parts before!

DOCTOR: I had not heard of it. Do you keep this pearl in a safe place? Perhaps you would like me to put it in my safe for you?

KINO (*frowning*): I have it secure. Tomorrow I will sell it, and then I will pay you.

(*The* DOCTOR *shrugs. He looks carefully into* KINO'*s face.*)

DOCTOR: It would be a shame to have it stolen before you could sell it.

(KINO'*s eyes flick involuntarily towards the place where the pearl is buried. The* DOCTOR *looks quickly at the* SERVANT.)

DOCTOR: Very well! Of course I will trust you to pay me when you have sold your pearl. If the baby is a little sick again, do not worry.

(He goes to the door and turns again.)

DOCTOR: Naturally, should you feel it is necessary for me to call again, you have only to send word.

(He gives an ingratiating smile to KINO *and a nod to* JUANA. *The* SERVANT *also smiles falsely and nods as he follows the* DOCTOR *out with the bag and lantern.* KINO *goes to the door and gazes out.* JUANA *picks the baby out from the cradle and settles with him by the fire.* KINO *returns and rolls out the sleeping mats. Then he looks across at where the pearl is buried. 'The Song of the Pearl' begins very quietly.* KINO *crosses to the hiding-place, digs up the pearl, and returns with it, burying it again, this time under the head of the sleeping-mat.* JUANA *watches him with questioning eyes.)*

JUANA: Kino, who is it that you fear?

(He searches for an honest answer, then makes a gesture of bafflement.)

KINO: Everyone.

(After a moment's stillness, they lie down to sleep. The last light from the embers glows on the walls of the hut before the darkness swallows them. Music: 'The Song of the Pearl', first on a solo instrument, then building up to a crescendo as other instruments join in. After a moment or two, as the music reaches its climax, we witness KINO's *dream: in a ghostly spotlight, a young* BOY, *dressed like* KINO *in a white shirt, is sitting at a school desk, writing. After a few moments he stops and takes out a large book, and begins to read. His mouth moves, but we hear no words. It is* COYOTITO, *aged eight or nine. After a short time the dream is disturbed by the 'Song of Evil', played very loudly against 'The Song of the Pearl'. The effect is one of discord – the dream turning to nightmare. In front of the boy, obscuring him, the characters of*

the PRIEST, *the* DOCTOR *and the* MERCHANTS *appear, but they are wearing grotesque exaggerations of their features in the form of masks or carnival heads. They circle the boy, and close in. They shake their heads and look and leer at one another. They begin to point accusing fingers and mime laughter. They take the book from* COYOTITO *and hold it up, mocking his reading. All their movements are ugly and distorted – a kind of evil dance. At the moment of loudest cacophony there is a sudden blackout and silence.*

In the hut, a narrow slanting beam of light falls dimly on KINO's *head. In the silence, there is a rustling noise, from the corner of the hut.* KINO *sits up. Silence. The noise begins furtively again. A* THIEF *is in the brush house.* JUANA *is awake also.* KINO *draws his knife. The blade glints. With a howl of anger* KINO *leaps at the darkness in the corner of the hut. There is the sound of blows and confused fighting, then a cry of pain. The shadowy figure of the* THIEF *scurries away.* JUANA *moves. She lights a little candle.* KINO *returns slowly to her. His forehead and face are covered with blood.* JUANA *moans softly, but she reaches for water quickly and at once she is soothing him and swabbing the blood from the wound on his forehead.*)

KINO (*painfully*): It is nothing.
JUANA: The wound is not too deep. There will be a big bruise, though.
KINO: He was inside the house. He was digging for the pearl.
JUANA (*the tension that has been building up inside her breaking out*): This pearl is like a sin! It will destroy us. Throw it away, Kino. Let us break it between stones. Let us bury it and forget. It has brought evil. Kino, my husband, it will destroy us.
KINO (*his face set*): This is our one chance, Juana. Our son must break out of the pot that holds us in!
JUANA (*anguished*): But don't you see! Even our son. It will destroy us all!

(*Blackout and silence.*)

CHORUS 8

(*'The Music of Dawn'. An empty stage. Sunrise on the backcloth. The members of the Chorus arrive one by one, including the* BEGGARS *and* KINO'*s* NEIGHBOURS, *collecting and clustering in small groups. Moving rapidly across the stage, individuals split away and join other groups. They carry various props, the goods or tools for the day's work. There could be someone on an old bicycle. Movement, excitement, expectation – the visual effect should echo the urgency of the spoken words. In the brush house, unobtrusively,* KINO *and* JUANA *prepare for the expedition to the city,* JUANA *combing and braiding her hair with red ribbons.*)

NEIGHBOURS: Today . . .
Today . . .
Today . . .
Today . . .
Today is the day that Kino will sell his pearl.
Today he will go to the buyers in the town.
Today one man who was like you and me will be changed.
Today Kino will sell his pearl and become a rich man.

Today is a day set apart from others.
Today is the day from which others will take their name:
Juana will say, 'It was two years from the day we sold the pearl.'
And Kino will speak to his friends in this way:
'Such a time was two years before we had sold the pearl.'

BEGGARS: But let him beware!
It is known for wealth to turn a good man's head.
Let it not graft on him the evil limbs of cold and hatred.
This Kino is known to be an honest man.
He has a good wife, Juana; a beautiful child –
Let them beware lest this pearl should destroy them all!

He will surely imagine the dealers in town will
pay a great price for this pearl.
But let him beware!
There is one fat man in the city who pulls their
strings:
all the buyers in town are puppets to this one
man.

(*One* BEGGAR *deftly takes a jacket from the arm of one of the* NEIGHBOURS, *a hat or cigar from another, and dresses himself as the fat business man. A third borrows a chair or stool for him to sit on.*)

BEGGARS: Already he calls them into his office and says:
BEGGAR (*in character*): Enter!

(*The stage lighting darkens, leaving a spotlight on and around the* BEGGAR *into which the three real* BUYERS *enter.*)

BEGGAR: I have heard that today a fisherman from the shore houses is coming to town with a great pearl, a priceless pearl. These men are superstitious. A little money is a great thing to such as this Kino. If it is worth ten thousand pesos offer him one; if it is worth twenty thousand, offer him fifteen. You know your job. If you do well today there may be a raise for you. Say ten per cent of the difference. (*Barks*) Do you understand?

(*The* BUYERS *look at each other, nod and exit. The lights return to their former setting, and the owners of the jacket, the chair etc. reclaim them.*)

NEIGHBOURS: This is foolish talk. Today is a joyful day.
Today there must be no talk of cheating and
fraud.
For today is the day when Kino will go to the
town to sell his pearl.

A day that the poorest among us can share.
Today is the day of Kino's happiness.
Today is the day that Kino will go to redeem
the Pearl of the World.

SCENE 9 *The brush house and the beach. Morning.*

(*The lights concentrate our attention on the brush house.* JUANA *puts on her headshawl carefully and gathers the long ends together as a sling to carry the baby, which she takes from the hanging cradle.* KINO *is trying the angles for his broad-brimmed straw hat, using a small mirror on one wall.* JUAN TOMÁS *and* APOLONIA, *dressed in their best clothes, enter excitedly.* APOLONIA *crosses to* JUANA.)

APOLONIA (*admiring* JUANA): Ah, Kino, but she is beautiful!

(KINO *smiles; the gloom of the previous evening gone.* APOLONIA *peeks at the baby.*)

APOLONIA: And Senor Coyotito! Such a brave little fisherman! Is he better today?

JUANA: The Doctor's medicine was good. There is still a little swelling, but it is not fiery around the bite now.

APOLONIA: And he is so smart!

JUANA (*embarrassed*): They are the clothes I was saving for his baptism. But when there will be money for his baptism, well . . .

(*She smiles and makes a gesture to indicate 'what does it matter'.*)

APOLONIA: Ah, such a baptism it will be. And such a wedding too! You must have them on the same day! It will be better than all the festivals and the carnival together! (*To* KINO) Are you nervous?

KINO: There is only one Pearl of the World. Let the buyers be nervous.

JUAN TOMÁS: Do you have the pearl safe?

KINO (*indicating a little leather bag on a thong around his neck*): I have it safe. Wrapped in deerskin.

JUAN TOMÁS: You must be careful to see that they do not cheat you.

KINO: I shall be careful.

JUAN TOMÁS: Yet we cannot know what prices are paid in other places. How can we know what is a fair price, if we do not know what a pearl buyer gets for a pearl in another place?

(KINO *stoops to pick up his blanket, which he folds carefully and drapes in a narrow strip over his shoulder.*)

KINO: That is true, but how can we know? We are here; we are not there.

JUAN TOMÁS (*pushing back his own hat and wiping his brow*): Before you were born, Kino, the old ones thought of a way to get more money for their pearls. They thought it would be better if they had an agent who took all the pearls to the capital and sold them there, and took only his share of the profit.

KINO (*nods*): I know. It was a good thought.

JUAN TOMÁS: And so they got such a man, and they pooled the pearls and they started him off. He was never heard of again, and the pearls were lost. Then they got another man, and they started him off, and he was never heard of again. In the end, they gave the whole thing up and went back to the old way.

KINO: This I know also. I have often heard our own father tell of it.

APOLONIA: It was a good idea, but it was against religion. The Priest has made that very clear. It was a punishment. They lost their pearls because they tried to leave their station. The Father says that each man and woman is like a soldier sent by God to guard some part of the castle of the universe. And some are in the ramparts, and some are far deep in the darkness of the walls, but each one must remain faithful to his post and not go running about, else the castle is in danger from the assaults of hell.

JUAN TOMÁS: I have heard him make that sermon more than once. He makes it every time there is some kind of trouble in the air.

(*There is a silence. They all look at one another.*)

JUAN TOMÁS (*cheerfully again*): Well! You are ready, then?

(KINO *and* JUANA *glance at each other and smile. Then* KINO *and* JUAN TOMÁS *step out into the roadway, followed by* JUANA *and* APOLONIA. *There is a cheer from the gathered* NEIGHBOURS *and a procession forms spontaneously behind them as they make their way, through the auditorium, if possible.*

Music: 'The Procession'. The procession includes the NEIGHBOURS, BEGGARS, CHILDREN, *even some of the* MUSICIANS. *There is an air of festival with animated talking. Someone might try a cartwheel – anything that fits the mood of the moment. If there are any small children in the Chorus, two of them are left on stage playing 'five stones' with little pebbles. When the procession has gone from the auditorium, they look up, realise they have been left behind, and rush off after the rest.*)

SCENE 10 *The Pearl Buyer's Office.*

(*While the procession is returning, possibly through another door of the auditorium, the first pearl* BUYER *sets up his desk in a spotlight downstage. On the desk, there is a vase with a single bloom, and a black velvet pearl tray. As he waits, he hums and rolls a coin back and forth across his knuckles. He is a stout, fatherly man, full of apparent friendliness, which he puts on as a mask for his real business, self-*

interest. The procession arrives and gathers outside the BUYER'*s office. There is a hush of expectancy.* KINO *steps into the spotlight, along with* JUAN TOMÁS. *The others push in to the edge of the light.*)

BUYER: Good morning, my friend. What can I do for you?
KINO (*after a pause*): I have a pearl.

(*The* BUYER *is nervous: he goes on turning the coin in his fingers.*)

BUYER: You have a pearl. Sometimes a man brings in a dozen. Well, let us see your pearl. We will value it and give you the best price.

(KINO, *who knows how to make the most of a dramatic effect, slowly lifts the thong from his neck and undoes the pouch. He unwraps the pearl and lets it roll across the* BUYER'*s tray, his eyes watching the* BUYER'*s intently for a sign of his response. The* BUYER'*s face gives away nothing, but the coin slips in his fingers and falls to the ground. His hand curls into a fist. It unwinds like a snake and slowly, very slowly, reaches out and touches the pearl. He rolls it in the tray, then picks it up between his forefinger and thumb. He holds it and rotates it in front of his face. The crowd hold their breath. A whisper runs back.*)

CHORUS: He is inspecting it.
No price has been mentioned.
They have not yet come to a price . . .

(*At last the* BUYER *throws it down in the tray. He smiles sadly, shrugging his shoulders a little.*)

BUYER: I am sorry, my friend.
KINO (*after a hesitation*): It is a pearl of great value.
BUYER (*flicking it idly across the tray*): You have heard of fool's gold. This pearl is like fool's gold. It is too large. Who would buy it? There is no market for such things. It is a

curiosity only. I am sorry. You thought it was a thing of value, and it is only a curiosity.

KINO (*his face dark with perplexity*): It is the Pearl of the World! No-one has ever seen such a pearl!

BUYER: On the contrary. It is large and clumsy. As a curiosity it has interest. Some museum might perhaps take it to place in a collection of sea-shells. I can give you, say, a thousand pesos.

KINO: It is worth fifty thousand! You know it. You want to cheat me!

(*A murmur of discontent passes through the crowd.*)

BUYER (*quickly*): You cannot blame me. I am only an appraiser. Ask the others. Go to their offices and show the pearl. Or better – let them come here, so that you can see there is no collusion. (*He calls*) Boy!

(*The* BUYER *writes two names on a piece of paper. His* SERVANT *appears behind him.*)

BUYER: Boy, go to such a one, and such another. Ask them to step in here and do not tell them why. Just say that I will be pleased to see them.

(*As the* SERVANT *goes, he pulls another coin from his pocket and begins his sleight of hand again. The crowd begin to whisper quite audibly.*)

CHORUS: It was always possible that this would happen.
The pearl is large, but they say it has a strange colour.
I was suspicious of it straightaway . . .
He offered him a thousand pesos.
Some of us work a lifetime for a thousand pesos.
Suppose he takes it: yesterday he had nothing.

The dealer knew straightaway it was not a proper pearl. (*etc.*)

(*Music: a snatch of 'The Song of the Enemy', cut off by the return of the* SERVANT *with the other two* BUYERS. *The crowd parts to let them through. The* BUYERS *stand beside the desk, but do not glance at each other or the pearl.*)

BUYER: I have put a value on this pearl. The owner here does not think it fair. I will ask you to examine this – this thing, and make an offer. (*To* KINO) Notice, I have not mentioned what I have offered.

(*The* 2ND BUYER *takes the pearl and rolls it between his thumb and forefinger, then throws it down into the tray with a sneer.*)

2ND BUYER: I'm afraid you can't include me in this discussion. I will make no offer at all. I do not want it. This is not a pearl; it is a monstrosity. Better pearls are made of paste. I know these things. It is soft and chalky. It will lose its colour and die in a few months. (*To the* 3RD BUYER) Look at it if you will.

(*The* 3RD BUYER *picks it up and examines it with a pocket lens. He shows* KINO *the surface of the pearl under the lens.*)

3RD BUYER: You see how it looks when the surface is magnified?

(KINO *frowns.*)

3RD BUYER: Now you can see what we mean. Look at all the little marks and blemishes. (*With affected kindliness*) You must be disappointed. To you it would at first appear quite valuable? Well, such is the way of things: we cannot all be experts in everything. You are a fisherman. We dealers should not be so good in a fishing boat. (*After a pause*) Look, one of my clients has a liking for such unusual things. I will offer you five hundred pesos. (*Laughing*) Then I must hope I can sell it to him for six. It is a risk!

(KINO *reaches quickly and snatches the pearl from his hand. He wraps it in the deerskin and thrusts the pouch inside his shirt.*)

1ST BUYER (*standing*): I am a fool, I know, but my first offer stands. I still offer one thousand.

(KINO *turns to go.*)

1ST BUYER: What are you doing?
KINO (*fiercely*): I am cheated! My pearl is not for sale here. I will go, perhaps even to the capital.

(*He pushes his way out. The* BUYERS *glance at one-another.*)

1ST BUYER (*shouting after him*): I might go to fifteen hundred!

(KINO *pushes through the crowd who are shocked into silence.* JUANA *follows him. The rest remain watching them. The spotlight fades quickly. Music: 'The Song of the Enemy'. The* BUYERS *remove the furniture as they exit.*)

CHORUS 9

In the town,
In the town it is always like this.
The pearl is a fortune.
The pearl is paste.
The pearl is worth nothing.
And how can we tell?
To take what is offered,
To take a chance.

Which buyer is honest?
And which is a rogue?
They speak the same language.
So how can we tell
If the dealers are crooked,
their act pre-arranged?
Is Kino not foolish?
Is Kino not brave?
Is the poor man not cheated
the whole of his days?

SCENE 11 *The brush house. Evening.*

(*The lights rise on the brush house.* KINO, JUAN TOMÁS *and* JUANA *are seated on the floor.* JUAN TOMÁS *and* JUANA *are eating.* KINO *is deep in thought.*)

JUAN TOMÁS: You have the pearl safe?

(KINO *does not answer.*)

JUANA: He has buried it under the stone, there by the fire.
JUAN TOMÁS: That is good. There are many thieves.
JUANA (*with dread in her voice*): Last night, there was someone. Inside the house. It was too dark to see who; it was not a fisherman. You have noticed the wound on Kino's face.

(JUAN TOMÁS *nods. He looks at* KINO. *There is a long silence.*)

JUAN TOMÁS: You are not hungry?
KINO (*looking up at him at last*): Yesterday, two days ago, I had no enemies. Today I am not certain which of my neighbours I can trust. There is only you, my brother – and Apolonia. And the rest . . . (*He pauses*) There is this world, here, by the water. And there is the capital. All my life I have

lived with the wash of the sea in my hearing. I have been to the town. The capital is more than the town. The capital is beyond the mountains; two hundred miles. There will be many streets, and every man there will be a stranger. Where shall we eat? Where shall we sleep? (*Another pause. He speaks simply, but it is hard for him to say*) Juan Tomás, I am afraid.

JUAN TOMÁS: You do not have to go to the capital, Kino. You can go back to the town. Tell them you have changed your mind. One thousand five hundred pesos is a great deal of money. More than anyone here has ever seen. Maybe you can even push them to a little more . . .

KINO: I have a dream. And my dream is real: they will not destroy it. I have found the Pearl of the World, Juan Tomás. For me, for Coyotito, for Juana, the old life is ended; we are almost there . . . I have said it. I will go. Tomorrow I will go.

(*There is another profound silence.*)

KINO (*in a burst of exasperation*): In the town today they were cheats! What else could I do?

JUAN TOMÁS (*rising to his feet*): It is hard to know. We are cheated from birth to the day they overcharge us for our coffins. But we survive. You have defied more than the pearl buyers. You have defied the whole structure, the whole way of life. I, too, am afraid, for you.

KINO (*almost sneering at himself*): It was my own thought. It was weakness. What have I to fear but starvation?

JUAN TOMÁS: That we must all fear. But suppose you are correct. Suppose your pearl is of great value. Do you think, then, the game is over?

KINO: What do you mean?

JUAN TOMÁS: It is new ground you are walking on. You do not know the way.

KINO: I will go. Anything else is impossible now.

JUAN TOMÁS: I understand. But I wonder if you will find it any different in the capital? Here, at least, you have friends, and me, your brother. There you will have no-one.

KINO: What can I do! (*He strikes his chest*) It is here in my heart – a great outrage. My son must have a chance!

(*Again, there is a deep silence.*)

JUAN TOMÁS: Go with God.

(*He turns and exits quietly.*)

KINO (*a chilly echo in his voice*): Go with God.

(*Silence.* KINO *stares emptily in front of him.* JUANA *gathers up the plates. There is a little whimpering cry from the basket cradle.* JUANA *goes to the cradle and rocks it. Very gently, but clearly and confidently, she begins to sing 'A Lullaby'. As she sings, the lights concentrate slowly down to a single small follow-spot on* KINO. *It is as if he is surrounded by darkness and* JUANA*'s song is fighting to keep it away.*)

JUANA (*sings*):

Go to sleep, sweet baby mine,
Your mother's spinning a thread so fine;
You daddy's over the mountains gone,
Gone to buy shoes for his little one.
Pretty shoes with buckles bright,
Sleep, baby mine, all night.

Go to sleep, sweet baby mine,
Your mother will watch and keep you from harm;
You'll see daddy back when the morning comes,
Bringing those shoes for his little one.
Pretty shoes with buckles bright,
Sleep, baby mine, all night.

Scene 11 The brush house. Evening

(*After the song has been heard clearly once through, against it, quietly at first but rising, is 'The Song of the Enemy'.* JUANA *continues to sing, fighting against the evil of the other music.* KINO *can hear the dark things beyond the brush house, creeping, moving, waiting for him to go out into the night. His hand goes to his knife. He draws it and the blade flashes in the light.* JUANA *stops singing. For a moment, she rushes to where he is standing, but he steps away through the 'door' of the brush house and the spot follows him. Night on the backcloth. 'The Song of the Enemy' begins to fragment. It is now several, separate percussion sounds, rasping, hissing, mocking him from different places about the stage.* KINO *hears one sound and rushes towards it. It stops and another calls him. Again he rushes towards it, the spot following. The audience almost catch sight of shadowy figures. As he rushes again and again the* ROBBERS *slink away like hyenas. He cannot quite catch any of them.*)

KINO (*shouting*): Who are you? Who are you? Who are you? Vermin! I am Kino! I am Kino!

(*As he shouts, the sounds begin to cease. The last shout rings out in an eerie silence, broken only by the wash of the sea. For a long time, he stands rigid with anger, listening, like an animal. At last he goes back to the brush house and the lights rise on the interior.* JUANA *is waiting in fear.*)

JUANA (*after a pause*): What is it?
KINO: I don't know. I couldn't see.

(*He reaches for his sleeping mat and unrolls it beside the fire. He slumps down on it dejected. There is another silence.*)

JUANA: Kino, my husband.

(*There is real anguish in her voice, but* KINO *does not respond. He seems to stare past her.*)

JUANA: Kino, can you hear me?
KINO (*dully*): I hear you.
JUANA (*kneeling, pleading*): Kino, this pearl is evil. Let us destroy it before it destroys us. Let us throw it back into the sea where it belongs. Kino, it is evil! It is evil!
KINO (*rising to kneel opposite her, his eyes glowing*): No! I will fight this thing. I will win over it. We will have our chance. (*Fiercely*) No-one shall take our good fortune from us! (*More gently, placing his hands on* JUANA*'s shoulders*) Believe me. I am a man. In the morning we will take our canoe and we will go over the sea and over the mountains to the capital, you and I. We will not be cheated.
JUANA (*huskily*): Kino, I am afraid. A man can be killed. Let us throw the pearl back in the sea.
KINO (*fiercely again*): Hush! I am a man. Hush!

(JUANA *is silent.*)

KINO: Let us sleep a little. In the first light we will start. You are not afraid to go with me?

(*Gently he touches her cheek.*)

JUANA: No, my husband.

(*Lights fade quite slowly on the brush house.*)

CHORUS 10

(*Perhaps just three of the Chorus:* YOUNG WOMEN *of* JUANA*'s age.*)

There was peace once
and the fire burned with its slow smoke
in the little hearth of the brush house.

There was peace once
and the song of the life of the village
drifted like skeins of smoke on the simple air.

There was peace once
and you lifted your baby up to the smile of the sun,
and you dandled his feet in the streams that run down on the
shore.

There was peace once
in the heart of the girl who grew up in the sound of the waves,
in the heart of the girl who had scarcely stepped ten
miles from the place where her mother and father were born.

There was peace once
but that peace is gone now forever:
in its place the pearl that your husband won from the sea.

So now you creep to the stone
where the pearl is hidden.
To steal back a time that you know can never be.

SCENE 12 *The beach and the brush house. Night.*

(Moonlight shines on the backdrop. There is just enough light in the brush house for us to see JUANA *creep soundlessly from her bed beside* KINO *towards the fireplace. Carefully she moves the stone where* KINO *has concealed the pearl. She moves it with the slightest noise.* KINO *opens his eyes but does not move.* JUANA *takes the pearl and replaces the stone, turns to look for a moment at the baby's basket cradle and then steps like a shadow out through the door. After a moment,* KINO *rises from his bed and follows her.*

The sound of the waves is heard. The lights change to suggest the moonlight outside. JUANA *is on the shore. She is hesitating. She holds the pearl up to the light of the moon. It is as if she is afraid of its power. She is not aware of* KINO *who crouches like a cat in the shadows.* JUANA *turns away from the sea. She takes two or three steps as if to return to the brush house. Then with a sudden moment of courage she turns again and runs forward to throw the pearl as far as she can out into the waves.* KINO *springs, like an animal, as before. He catches her arm as she flings it back for the throw. She squeals with pain.* KINO *wrenches the pearl from her fist, then very cruelly and quite deliberately he strikes her with a clenched blow across her face which knocks her to the ground.* JUANA *cries out again, but it is a stifled cry.* KINO *is beside himself with rage, transformed and ugly. He hisses at her.*)

KINO: Woman!

(JUANA *lifts herself up, about to try to rise to her feet. As she does so,* KINO *strikes at her a second time and as she falls he kicks her in the side.*)

KINO: Woman!

(*There is a pause.* JUANA *rolls back to face* KINO. *She pushes up on one hand, but this time she does not attempt to rise. She simply looks at him with wide unfrightened eyes. There is a moment of terrible silence between them, held as long as possible. Then the fierce tension in* KINO *breaks and his body relaxes as the rage leaves him. It is replaced by a flood of sick disgust. He turns away from her and walks slowly, emptily towards the shadows and the brush house.* JUANA*'s head falls. She remains still where she lies and the pool of moonlight surrounding her fades.*

Spatterings of moonlight around and within the brush house. KINO *stops just outside the door. His hand goes to his knife. Music: 'The Song of the Enemy', a loud, heavy beat. The following sequence takes place in semi-darkness: there are shadowy figures, noises, confusion. There are three* ROBBERS, *two of whom are inside the house. The* 1ST ROBBER *leaps at* KINO *from the doorway,* KINO *pushes him back and draws his knife. The blade glints. The* 1ST ROBBER *lunges again.* KINO*'s knife goes home and he falls just outside the doorway. The* 2ND ROBBER *appears in the doorway. Crouching down,* KINO *threatens him with a sweep of the knife blade. The* 3RD ROBBER *steps from the shadows behind him and takes him by the throat.* KINO *is beaten to the ground. The knife and the pearl fall from* KINO*'s hands. The* 2ND *and* 3RD ROBBERS *search his unconscious body for the pearl. The sound of crying is heard from* COYOTITO*'s basket cradle. Finding nothing, the two remaining* ROBBERS *go back into the brush house. One examines the body of their companion briefly, but finding him dead, he carries on. They search the brush house, pulling it apart violently. One searches in the cradle but does not harm or remove the baby. The sound of crying redoubles. Finally they make their exit towards the beach. They stop by* KINO*'s canoe with their backs to the auditorium. The noise of wood smashing and splintering is heard.*

'The Song of the Enemy' fades. There is silence except for the baby whimpering. A long pause follows. The moonlight shines on JUANA. JUANA *shakes her head and painfully drags herself to her feet. She limps across to the point where the fight took place. For a moment she recoils and is puzzled. Then she recognises* KINO, *and that the other man is dead. She kneels beside* KINO *and tries to revive him.* KINO *groans.* JUANA *looks around: she is terrified, but her mind is racing. She rests* KINO*'s head back on the ground and moves across to the body of the* ROBBER. *She picks up* KINO*'s knife and wipes the blade on the dead man's clothes. She puts down the knife beside* KINO *and as she does so she sees the pearl glint on the ground. She picks it up. A bitter smile flickers across her face. Then she casts it down hurriedly beside* KINO *and the knife and sets about the business of dragging the body away from the doorway into the darkness behind the brush house. As she returns,* KINO *tries to sit up. He moans incoherently.* JUANA *fetches a bottle from the house and puts it to* KINO*'s lips. He is still too*

confused to drink. She pours the remainder of the liquid over his face and shakes him.)

JUANA: Kino! Kino, my husband!

(KINO *grunts and opens his eyes and looks at her.*)

KINO (*heavily*): They have taken the pearl. I have lost it. Now it is over. The pearl is gone.

JUANA (*as if she is quieting a child*): Here is your pearl. It was lying on the path. Can you hear me now? Here is your pearl. Can you understand? Listen! You have killed a man. We must go away. The police, the soldiers, they will come for us – can you understand? We must be gone before the daylight comes.

KINO (*uneasily*): I was attacked. I struck to save my life.

JUANA: Do you remember yesterday? Do you think that will matter? Do you remember the men of the city? Do you think they will believe you when you explain?

KINO (*shaking himself and rising unsteadily*): No. You are right. Bring Coyotito, and bring all the corn that we have. We will go now. I will drag the canoe into the water and we will go.

(JUANA *runs into the house.* KINO *hides the pearl in the pouch round his neck, picks up his knife and strides into the darkness towards the beach. There is a pause and we are aware in the dim light of* JUANA *gathering the things for the journey and wrapping the baby into her shawl to carry him. She turns to take one last look around the devastated brush house. Suddenly there is a howl of anguish from the darkness of the shore. The lights change and reveal* KINO *on the beach with the damaged canoe, a great gaping jagged hole in its hull.* JUANA *runs into this pool of light, clutching* KINO*'s shoulder blanket and his hat, as well as the baby and the food she has gathered.* KINO *is crouching, head in hands. He beats his fists on the ground in frustration and sorrow.*)

KINO: Why? Tell me why do they do such a thing? It was *my* boat – my father's boat. And his father's before him. But a boat has no sons. A boat cannot protect itself. A wounded boat cannot heal. This is evil. This is the last evil thing!

(But even as he speaks we hear the crackling sound of fire. Lights on the backcloth or in the brush house area suggest a fire, growing in intensity. A smoke machine or dry ice may also be used. Music: 'The Music of Evil'. The couple turn, becoming aware of the flames.)

JUANA: It is our house, Kino. That is the last thing. They tore it apart, even the floor.
KINO: But they found no pearl.
JUANA: And now they have returned, with fire. As I ran, I saw them setting their torches to the house.
KINO: Who?
JUANA: I couldn't see. The dark ones.

(The stage is overwhelmed with the PEOPLE OF THE VILLAGE *running to the scene of the fire, shouting and calling to one another. Some form a bucket chain, some beat out sparks with brooms. There is confusion.* KINO *and* JUANA *slip away. The brush house is pulled apart as the* CHORUS *effect the changes to the setting necessary for the following scenes.)*

SCENE 13 *Juan Tomás' house.*

(Darkness. The dying flicker of flames is seen on the backcloth. 'The Song of the Enemy' has gone and the confusion has subsided into a low, persistent keening from a group of the CHORUS WOMEN *who remain huddled with their backs to the audience, upstage, still watching the remains of the fire. A dim circle of light well downstage and away from the position of* KINO'*s house picks out* JUAN TOMÁS' *house. A few furnishings suggest an interior not unlike* KINO'*s*

house. KINO *and* JUANA *slip into* JUAN TOMÁS' *house.* KINO *wraps his blanket around* JUANA. *They huddle in a 'corner' as if hiding. The keening continues, led by* APOLONIA. *After a minute or so,* APOLONIA *breaks away and returns to the house. She runs in and opens a box or chest and begins to change her headshawl for her best one. She does not notice the motionless figures. When* KINO *speaks, she spins round and utters a little stifled cry.*)

KINO: Apolonia, do not cry out. We are not hurt.
APOLONIA: But are you not dead? Are you not burned alive in your brush house? How do you come here?
KINO: Do not question. Go now to Juan Tomás and bring him here and tell no-one else. This is important to us, Apolonia.

(*She looks at them for a moment, as if to make sure they are not ghosts. Then speaks.*)

APOLONIA: Yes, my brother-in-law.

(*She goes. There is a minute before she returns with* JUAN TOMÁS. JUANA *rocks the baby.* KINO *puts his arm round her shoulders, as much to comfort himself as to comfort* JUANA. *When* JUAN TOMÁS *and* APOLONIA *enter, nothing is said at first.* JUAN TOMÁS *lights a candle. It illuminates the four faces as they talk in whispers.*)

JUAN TOMÁS: Apolonia, see to the door, and let no-one come in.

(*He regards* KINO *gravely for a moment.*)

JUAN TOMÁS: Now, my brother.
KINO: I was attacked in the dark. And in the fight I have killed a man.
JUAN TOMÁS: Who?
KINO: I don't know. It is all darkness – all darkness and the shape of darkness.

JUAN TOMÁS: It is the pearl. There is a devil in this pearl. You should have sold it and passed on the devil. Perhaps you can sell it and buy peace for yourself.

KINO: That may be. But oh, my brother, an insult has been put on me that is deeper than my life, for on the beach my canoe is broken. And now my house is burned. And a dead man lies in the shadows of the brush. Every escape is cut off. You must hide us, my brother.

(JUAN TOMÁS *says nothing, but the silence is significant.*)

KINO: Not for long. In the first light of the dawn we shall be gone.

JUAN TOMÁS: I will hide you.

KINO (*rising*): I do not want to bring danger to you. We will go now, and then you will be safe.

JUAN TOMÁS (*his hand on* KINO'*s shoulder*): We will protect you. Tomorrow I shall say, 'I think they have gone south, along the coast. Maybe they found another boat.'

APOLONIA: And I shall cry and weep for you, as if you were dead. There is a wind blowing up off the sea tonight. They will think if you went to sea you are surely drowned.

KINO: We will go north. I have heard there are cities in the north.

(*There is a silence.* JUAN TOMÁS *goes to the door and looks out. There is the sound of the wind, rising. This sound is a background noise, but it continues for the following scene.*)

APOLONIA (*to* JUANA): You will need food. And warm things for the baby.

(*She bustles around and brings out various items. Her voice is trying to maintain a cheerful tone, but she is holding back tears.*)

APOLONIA: Some red beans. You must keep the little bag; it

was my sister's, she gave it to me before our wedding. And this is good rice. It will make a good meal with a little water. You must take some peppers. And salt. Take this block of salt . . . And for tomorrow, for the first part of the journey, you will not have time to stop, and you must not make a fire or they will see the smoke. It is a good thing I made corn-cakes for Juan Tomás – take them. Tomorrow we can fast; it will do us good . . .

(JUAN TOMÁS *steps back into the candlelight.*)

JUAN TOMÁS: You must avoid the shore. When they find the body, they will make a party to search the shore. They know you are a fisherman. They will bring men from the town. With guns, probably. (*Pauses*) Do you still have the pearl?

KINO (*bitterly*): I have it. And I will keep it. Once I might have given it as a gift, but now it is my misfortune and my life and I will keep it. The pearl has become my soul. If I give it up I shall lose my soul.

(JUAN TOMÁS *goes to a corner of the house. He brings out a knife wrapped carefully in a skin or a cloth. He unwraps it.*)

JUAN TOMÁS: It is a working knife; I have used it. It is heavy as an axe. You may need it. It is a good weapon also.

(KINO *tries the blade with his thumb. His eyes are alive with gratitude, but he can say nothing.* JUAN TOMÁS *goes to the door again. The first glimmers of the dawn light have replaced the fire effect on the backcloth. The sound of the wind grows in intensity.*)

JUAN TOMÁS: The wind is good. There will be no tracks.

(*Lights fade on* JUAN TOMÁS' *house.* APOLONIA *blows out the candle.*)

CHORUS 11

The wind blows, fierce and strong.
The wind blows, and the sand stings
in your face, in your eyes,
with its grains in your teeth,
but you bite them and spit
and you lower your head and walk on:
by the edge of the town,
by the dried-up stream,
by the road where only the carters go,
and you move like shadows across the land.

The wind blows, fierce and strong,
The wind blows and the sand sifts
in the tracks, in the ruts where the ox-carts go;
and you walk in file and your footprints
drift into shapeless dust,
and the sticks and the straws
scatter patterns across the empty road.

The wind blows, and it whisks and cries
in the brush as you walk,
and the baby wakes, but you soothe him
and hour after hour you walk on.
And each step that you take
is a step away from the men
who will come for your life,
who will come to take the Pearl of the World,
with their horses and sharp eyes and guns.

SCENE 14 *Foothills of the mountains. Day.*

(The mountains: scrubby vegetation, rocks, various levels. The sound of the wind is still present, though fading, as KINO *and* JUANA

enter. JUANA *walks two or three steps behind* KINO. *They are tired and* KINO *indicates that they will rest, a little way away from the road.* JUANA *settles herself and makes a place to settle the baby using* KINO's *blanket.* KINO *breaks off a branch (or finds one broken by the wind) and carefully sweeps away the footprints between their resting-place and the road. When* KINO *rejoins* JUANA, *he slumps down wearily.* JUANA *offers him a drink from a water bottle.*)

JUANA: Have we travelled well?

KINO: Fifteen miles. Eighteen maybe.

JUANA: Will they follow us? Can they find which way we have come?

KINO: They will try. When they find nothing on the shore, they will look for the roads into the mountains: there are only so many ways to go. And it is not just for me that they follow. Whoever finds us will take the pearl.

JUANA: Perhaps the dealers were right and the pearl has no value. Perhaps this has all been an illusion.

(KINO *reaches into his clothes and brings out the pearl. He holds it in front of him and lets the sun play on its surface.*)

KINO: No, they would not have tried to steal it if it had been valueless.

JUANA: Do you know who it was that attacked you? The dealers?

KINO: I cannot tell. It was too dark to be sure.

(KINO *looks deep into the pearl, like a man looking into a crystal ball. His words are optimistic, but the tone of his voice and the sorrow in his face seem to give the lie to his pronouncements.*)

KINO: When we sell it at last, I will have a rifle. (*Pause*) We will be married in a great church. (*Pause*) My son shall learn to read.

Scene 14 Foothills of the mountains. Day

(*Silence between them. Music: 'The Song of the Pearl', thin and drifting.* JUANA *turns and smiles at the baby. She gives him a little drink of water from the bottle. When she has settled the baby again,* JUANA *takes from her bundle one of* APOLONIA*'s corn-cakes, and breaks it in half.* KINO *thrusts the pearl back into his clothing.* JUANA *offers him one of the pieces which he takes and begins to eat. She returns the other to her pack. As* KINO *eats he is uneasy, listening.*)

JUANA: What is it?

(KINO *signals to her to be silent. He has stopped eating. He draws out the long knife.*)

JUANA (*After a pause*): What's the matter?
KINO: I don't know.

(KINO *is listening again, an animal light in his eyes. Silently he rises to his feet. He looks towards the baby.*)

KINO: Keep him quiet.

(*Crouching low,* KINO *threads his way back to the edge of the road, perhaps to a slightly raised level. He watches intently the direction from which they have come. Suddenly he has seen enough; he moves rapidly back to* JUANA *and the baby.*)

KINO: They are very close! Much nearer than I thought.
JUANA: How many?
KINO: Three. One of them has a horse, and a rifle. The others are hunters – trackers. The horse is tied up by the stream we crossed; they are all three moving up on foot.

(JUANA *takes* COYOTITO *quickly and wraps him again in her shawl.* KINO *gathers the rest of their belongings.*)

JUANA: Which way shall we go?

KINO: If we move now, they will see us. Hear us maybe. While they are on the road there is a chance they may go past. Then we will go up and over the ridge. These men could follow a sheep in the stone mountains: that is the way their people have lived. They can read signs as small as a broken straw; a pile of dust. It is possible they may see where I have swept with the branch. If that is so, I must try to take the one with the rifle. It is our only chance.

(KINO *and* JUANA *draw back so they are hidden from the road.* KINO *crouches with his toes dug into the ground, ready to strike. Turning her back to the audience,* JUANA *holds the baby close, apparently feeding him at her breast to keep him silent. Music: 'The Song of the Enemy'. The* 1ST TRACKER *enters at a run, but moving lightly, carefully. He crouches to examine the ground where* KINO *swept. The* 2ND TRACKER *joins him, followed by the* 3RD TRACKER *who halts behind them. They speak quietly but urgently – men with a purpose.*)

1ST TRACKER: There is something. They have been this way.

3RD TRACKER: How long ago?

1ST TRACKER: It is hard to tell. There are no prints, and they are trying to cover their tracks. But he is not a man of the hills: he does not know the hills as we do.

(*They scurry on a little and examine the ground again.*)

2ND TRACKER: If he is trying to get to the city, he will probably stick to the roads. He would be too slow otherwise. And probably they would go round in circles.

3RD TRACKER: It is still a day's journey before they are out of the mountains; then we shall be able to see them.

1ST TRACKER: The marks by the stream were fresh; they are not so far ahead. They must carry their baby: we are swift. Before nightfall we shall find them.

(The 3RD TRACKER *takes out a flask, swigs from it, and passes it to the others. They drink in turn and grin. Then they move on, slowly, examining the ground as they go. The* 1ST TRACKER *returns to the swept spot and looks carefully again. He listens, like an animal. Then he exits after the others quickly. After a long pause, during which 'The Song of the Enemy' rises and dies away,* KINO *and* JUANA *emerge.* KINO *looks cautiously up the road where the* TRACKERS *have gone.)*

KINO: They are gone now, but in a little while they will realise they have missed the path, and they will come back, searching, and find this place where we have hidden. From here it will be easy for them: the little stones, the broken leaves . . . Perhaps I should let them take me.

JUANA (*hoarsely*): You have the pearl. Do you think they would take you back alive to say they had stolen it?

KINO (*weakly*): Perhaps it is fate they will find it.

JUANA: There is no fate, Kino, only you and me and Coyotito. Do you think they would let *me* live? Do you think they would spare the little one?

KINO (*stung into action*): Come! We will go up towards the mountains. Maybe we can lose them in the mountains.

(They gather up their belongings and exit quickly. KINO *carrying the bundle in his left hand and the big knife swinging free in his right.)*

CHORUS 12

The little stones, the broken leaves . . .
Hot feet on the rocks that pulse with the sun's heat.

And soon there are no leaves,
there are no trees,
and the only shade is the shade
of the great forked cactus plants.

And you bow your head and press on,
though your tongue is dry
and the knives of the stones
have begun to flay your feet.

There is nothing here but the sun
and the strange high shapes of the rocks . . .
In the sand, the shed skin of a snake,
and the twitch of a lizard across your toes,
and the blaze of the sun in your face.

So then you know, in this dry land
that the night, if it comes, is your only friend.
When the sun dips and the shadows
swing in their arc to the east and grow long
there may still be an hour you can rest.

SCENE 15 *The mountains. Evening/night.*

(*Music: 'The Music of Evil', secret and poisonous, with an underlying heartbeat.* KINO *and* JUANA *struggle on to the stage over one of the raised 'rocks'. The lighting suggests very late evening with shadows and a reddish glow on the backdrop which fades quite quickly during the first part of the scene as the night encroaches. Somewhere above and apart from the main stage area there is a dark space – a cave. Hidden by rocks, but accessible to the actors, there is a small stream. As 'The Music of Evil' fades, the sound of water, very quiet, not rushing, is heard mixed with night sounds: tree frogs and cicadas.* KINO *and* JUANA *look exhausted, bedraggled, dusty.*)

JUANA: You were right. It's water!

(JUANA *slumps to her knees by the stream and, dipping in the edge of the shawl, bathes the baby's face. Then she fills her bottle and gives him a drink.* KINO *drinks long and thirstily from his cupped hands. Perhaps* JUANA *pours a little of the water from her bottle over his head: there is almost a sense of relief and release, but they are too tired to enjoy it.* KINO *stretches out on the ground and relaxes his aching limbs.)*

KINO: High in the mountains there is snow. Even in the hottest season there is snow on the shaded side of the mountains. And a little melts, so even in the desert there can be life. There are tracks and spoors of animals here.

(JUANA *looks worried.)*

KINO: While there are men they will stay away.
JUANA: How long can we stay here? We need to rest.
KINO (*shaking his head*): Not long. The trackers are not fools. They must know we can carry only a little water. When they see this cleft they will know. With an empty bottle there is no choice.

(JUANA *moves to sit by* KINO.)

KINO (*concerned, tender*): Your ankles are all cut with the stones and the thorns.
JUANA (*with a sad smile*): It is all like a dream: the kind of dream that comes with a fever. Maybe we shall wake soon . . .

(*A long silence, broken only by the sounds of the night.*)

KINO (*suddenly*): Juana, I will go and you will hide. I will lead them higher into the mountains, and when they have gone past, you will go north, to Loreto or Santa Rosalia. Then if I can escape them, I will come with you. It is the only way.
JUANA (*looking full into his eyes for a moment before she speaks*): No. We go with you.
KINO (*harshly*): I can go faster alone. You will put the little one in more danger if you go with me.

JUANA (*quietly but very clearly*): No.
KINO: You must. It is the wise thing, and it is my wish.
JUANA: No, my husband. Do not ask me again.

(KINO *looks intently into her face, as if searching for some sign of fear or weakness. She looks back at him, directly. Her eyes are bright, almost with tears. He moves close to her and with a gesture of great gentleness lifts his hand to touch her cheek. She continues to look directly into his eyes. He kisses her forehead, tenderly, as one might a child.* JUANA *looks down at the baby wrapped in the shawl. After a pause,* KINO *gets to his feet and moves carefully around the stage. He is surveying the immediate surroundings.*)

KINO: We will go west. Perhaps we can strike back towards the coast and that will deceive them.

(KINO *climbs back to check the direction from which they entered. He looks out and down. After a moment, he frowns and crouches. For a minute he continues to watch the distant figures of the* TRACKERS. *Then he turns back and moves quickly over to* JUANA, *who has been watching him.*)

JUANA (*quietly*): How far?
KINO: They will be here before the light is gone.

(KINO *pauses, weighing in his mind the balance of danger.*)

KINO: But there is one chance. Up there in the cliff there are hollows, little caves that the wind has made. Maybe, if we lie low and silent they will go past again. Fill up the water bottle.

(KINO *moves away and begins to climb up and over the rocks in the opposite direction from their entrance.*)

JUANA: What are you doing?

(KINO *puts his finger to his lips to indicate that she should be quiet. He disappears.* JUANA *gathers their belongings as best she can. Music: very quietly, 'The Song of the Enemy'.* JUANA *rocks the baby. After what seems an endless pause,* KINO *returns, picking his way more carefully than when he left. He speaks when he is close to* JUANA *again.*)

KINO: I have made a false trail, up to the next ledge. You see where the rock is smooth on this side? Tread carefully and leave no mark. We will hide in the cave hollow there. If we lie down, they will never see us. When they are gone over the ledge, we will slip away down to the lowlands again. I am afraid only that the baby may cry. You must see that he does not cry.

JUANA: He will not cry. (*Raising the baby up and looking solemnly into his face*) He knows.

(*Carefully,* KINO *helping as they go, they climb up to the cave and out of the fading stage light. The music increases in intensity: separate instruments bring in the themes of 'The Song of the Pearl' and 'The Song of the Family' – a tension of dissonant sound, which eventually cuts out to leave the eerie mountain silence. After a moment, we catch the* VOICES *of the* TRACKERS, *just before they enter from the same point as* KINO *and* JUANA*'s entrance.*)

2ND TRACKER: They cannot travel much more tonight, until the moon rises.

1ST TRACKER: There is water, listen.

(*There is a momentary pause before they arrive. Again the* 3RD TRACKER *follows the other two, warily. In addition to his rifle, he carries a storm lantern, unlit. They too fill their water bottles at the stream and drink. While the* 2ND TRACKER *is drinking, the* 1ST TRACKER *looks up at the rocks where* KINO *laid the false trail.*)

1ST TRACKER: There's something here. Look.

(*The* 2ND TRACKER *examines the ground carefully with him.*)

2ND TRACKER: Maybe they went up. They are getting desperate. (*To the* 3RD TRACKER) We need light.
3RD TRACKER: Why not wait for daylight? There is time. Tomorrow we have them.

(*The* 3RD TRACKER *taps the butt of his rifle.*)

2ND TRACKER: We would like to see.

(*Reluctantly, the* 3RD TRACKER *puts down his rifle and lights the lantern, which spreads a small circle in the gathering gloom. The* 2ND TRACKER *moves across and picks it up. Together with the* 1ST TRACKER *he examines the track up the cliff and the ground round about. The* 3RD TRACKER *sits down and takes out his flask and swigs from it.*)

1ST TRACKER: They were here. They rested here. You can see where they have been lying on the ground.
3RD TRACKER: How long ago?
2ND TRACKER: All this disturbance is very recent. They are tired now. They do not even bother to try to conceal their tracks. Maybe we should go on, to the next ledge, now.
3RD TRACKER: Sit down.

(*Reluctantly they comply: evidently he commands them like dogs.*)

3RD TRACKER: You are trackers, but you are not hunters.

(*He passes round the flask.*)

3RD TRACKER: I have hunted animals, and I have hunted men. It is the same thing: only a man is worth more than an animal. And this one . . .

1ST TRACKER: Maybe he does not still have the pearl.
3RD TRACKER: He has not sold it.
1ST TRACKER: He could have hidden it somewhere – buried it.
3RD TRACKER: He is a man. He will carry the pearl with him.
2ND TRACKER: And if not?
3RD TRACKER: You will still be paid. (*With a contemptuous laugh*) Not quite so much, but you will be paid.
2ND TRACKER (*eagerly*): We go on when the moon rises?
3RD TRACKER: No, my friend. We shall wait for the dawn. Even with the moon they will stumble about among the rocks. We shall be fresh in the morning. Lie down. Sleep a little. Tomorrow we make the kill.

(*The* 2ND TRACKER *shrugs his shoulders. The* 1ST TRACKER *returns the flask. They make pillows of whatever roll, pack or hat they may have, and stretch out. The* 3RD TRACKER *remains sitting. Idly, he takes a harmonica from his pocket and plays a few snatches of a tune, like 'Clementine'. After a few moments he stops playing, spits and returns the harmonica to his pocket. He turns the lamp light down.*)

CHORUS 13

So in the end, always it will come to this:
hunter and hunted, joined in the dark
by the long invisible thread of their fate
that is winding them closer and closer
until they come face to face,
and they know that the thread must break
and that one must die, and one must live.

And there's no way out, and they know at last
that what they wanted was not to be rich
or to keep the cattle safe on their land
or whatever it was they sought in their quest;
it was only this: to have fought and lived.

And now they are pitched like men with a coin
they must toss and the odds are life and death.

VOICE OF KINO (*whispering*): There is a way.
VOICE OF JUANA: But they will kill you.
VOICE OF KINO: If I get first to the one with the rifle . . . I must get to him first; then I will be all right. Two are sleeping.
VOICE OF JUANA: They will see your white clothes in the starlight.
VOICE OF KINO: No.

(KINO *removes his white shirt.*)

VOICE OF KINO: And I must go before moonrise. (*Pause*) If they kill me, lie quietly. And when they are gone away, go to Loreto.
VOICE OF JUANA: Kino!
VOICE OF KINO: There is no choice. It is the only way. They will find us in the morning.
VOICE OF JUANA (*trembling*): Go with God.

(*Briefly, at the cave mouth, their silent farewell. Music: 'The Song of the Family' [transposed into a minor key] and 'The Song of the Enemy' played separately on two instruments, but fragmented, then overlapping.* KINO *begins his descent from the cave. He has not gone far when the moon rises on the backdrop, cold and white. The* 3RD TRACKER *has risen to his feet and is watching the moonrise. He is unaware of* KINO *edging like a slow lizard towards him. When* KINO *reaches the stage level, he crouches in shadow. Ideally, there should still be ten or fifteen feet between him and the* 3RD TRACKER. *The music breaks off. Silence. Then from the cave, the short muffled cry of the baby. The* 3RD TRACKER *turns. The* 2ND TRACKER *wakes and turns up the lamp.*)

2ND TRACKER (*sleepy*): What is it?

3RD TRACKER: It sounded like a cry, almost human, like a baby.

2ND TRACKER: You can't tell. Some coyote bitch with a litter. I've heard a coyote pup cry like a baby.

(*Silence. The baby's cry again.*)

3RD TRACKER: Coyote, maybe. (*He cocks the rifle*) If it is a coyote, this will stop it.

(*He raises the gun and* KINO *leaps across the intervening space as the shot is fired. He is only fractionally too late. The following sequence is rapid and continuous, lit only by the lamp and silhouetted against the risen moon. Music: ad lib.* KINO'*s knife crashes down into the chest of* 3RD TRACKER. *He falls, and as he does so,* KINO *wrenches the rifle from his grasp. The* 2ND TRACKER *begins to rise, but is felled by a swinging blow with the butt of the rifle. The* 1ST TRACKER *scrabbles away like a crab towards the stream and the cliff. He begins to try to climb frantically.* KINO *turns, sees him, cocks the rifle and takes aim deliberately. He fires and the* TRACKER *falls with a cry.* KINO *strides across to the stream. The* TRACKER'*s head rises as he struggles to move.* KINO *shoots again. After the echoing of the last shot, there is sudden, complete silence.* KINO *returns to the circle of lamp light. Then, from the darkness of the cave, the keening, moaning, terrible cry of* JUANA *mourning for* COYOTITO.)

KINO (*anguished*): Juana!

(*The keening continues.*)

KINO: Coyotito!

(*'The Music of Evil'. Blackout.* KINO *picks up the lantern and moves towards the cave, extinguishing the lamp as he goes.*)

CHORUS 14

(Bright stage light, contrasting with the previous scene. As much of the mountain scenery removed and the original setting returned as is practicable. A crowd of the CHORUS *and cast on stage, but still.)*

In the town, in the villages, in the brush houses by the shore it is still told, the story of the great pearl – how it was found and lost again. They tell of Kino the fisherman, and of his wife, Juana, and of the baby that was shot and killed by the dark men in the mountains. And because the story has been told so often it has taken root in every man's mind. And, as with all re-told tales that are in people's hearts, there are only good and bad things, black and white things, the happy and evil things, and no in-between anywhere.

Everyone in La Paz remembers the return of the family; there may be some old ones who saw it, but those whose fathers and grandfathers told it to them remember it nevertheless.

It was late in the golden afternoon when the first little boys ran into the town and spread the word that Kino and Juana were coming back. The sun was settling towards the western mountains and the shadows on the ground were long as they stalked ahead. And they walked not one behind the other but side by side. And Juana carried her shawl like a sack on her shoulder, and the small, limp, heavy bundle swayed as she walked. And Kino carried a rifle across his arm.

SCENE 16 *The beach; The Village Dance. Late afternoon/evening.*

(KINO *and* JUANA *walk slowly down on to the stage and the crowd parts. The* MEN *remove their hats. The couple stand lit for a moment with the sunset behind them.* APOLONIA *takes the blood-stained bundle from* JUANA. JUAN TOMÁS *takes the rifle. Then they walk together to the edge of the stage that has represented the shore. They walk as though they are alone: their eyes glance neither right nor left but stare only straight ahead. At the edge they stop. There is the low sound of the sea.* KINO *digs among his clothes for the great pearl and holds it up and stares at it.*)

KINO: It shall go back. To the sea. It was my hope, my great hope. Now it is nothing. (*He pauses*) And all the time you knew.

(*His hand shakes a little as he turns to* JUANA *and holds the pearl out to her. She looks at the pearl in his hands for a moment, and then into his eyes.*)

JUANA: No. You.

(KINO *understands. He turns, draws back his arm and flings the pearl with all his might. As he does so, the lights black out. Music: 'The Song of the Pearl'. The slow rise of light on the backdrop shows* KINO *and* JUANA *in motionless silhouette as the music swells and fades leaving only the sound of the waves. The play ends with a folk dance – the* CHORUS OF VILLAGERS *begin.* KINO *and* JUANA *turn and watch. After a while the circle parts and they are accepted back into the symbolic ring. Lights dim again on the dance, which may also become the curtain-call.*)

THE END

QUESTIONS AND ASSIGNMENTS

Scene 1

Questions

1 What can Kino see and hear and smell as he looks out from his doorway on page 2? Describe the village and the shore in the early morning sunlight. What is going on? Are there people, animals, trees . . .? What mood is the sea in?
2 What dangers might there be for Kino when he is out diving near the reef?
3 Why are the people of the village surprised when Juana says they must send for a doctor for the baby? Why does the Doctor not usually come to the village?

Assignment

Before rehearsals, the Stage Manager must set out all the props and furniture in Kino's brush house. Draw a plan or sketch of the house, which is about 10 feet square, showing: the doorway, the fireplace, Coyotito's hanging basket, the sleeping mats, the water-jars, Juana's cooking-pots, and any other things you think they might need. (Remember that four or five actors often have to squeeze into this small space too, so you will need to leave room for them.)

Scene 2

Questions

1 What, do you think, have the Doctor and his wife been arguing about just before Scene 2?
2 Put yourself in the place of one of the beggars at the Doc-

tor's gate. What did you see when Kino and the villagers came to the gate? Did it turn out as you expected?

Assignment

Imagine you are the doctor's wife. Write a letter home to your mother or father. Explain why you are unhappy, and what you miss from the old life at home.

Scene 3

Question

Why has Juana prayed to the old, Mexican Gods *and* to the Christian figure of Mary (page 13)?

Scene 4

Assignments

Picture in your mind the undersea world of the reef where Kino is diving: the colours, the shapes, the creatures, the way they move, even the water itself – the bubbles and the surface above you. Try to write down every detail you can see in the picture in your mind. Write in short lines, one for each idea.

When you have completed your rough draft, work through it again. Try to make it into a simple free-verse poem. Listen to the sound of each line. Are there any words you can improve? Can you make them echo the sound of the undersea world? If you wish, you can include in your poem the moment when you discover the Pearl of the World, lying in its oyster shell.

Scene 5

Questions

1 Why does Kino leave the giant oyster to open last (page 16)?
2 What would it feel like to open the oyster and find the great pearl?

Assignments

1 Can you think of and describe a situation in which you would feel the same emotions as Kino did when he discovered the pearl?
2 People might react in different ways to suddenly becoming the most wealthy person in their village or town. In groups of two or three, devise and present a scene in which you show someone reacting in one particular way. Then replay the same scene showing a completely different way of reacting.

Scene 6

Questions

1 Look carefully at Chorus 6 (pages 16–17). What do the reactions to the news of Kino's good fortune tell us about:
  the Doctor,
  the Dealers,
  the Priest?
Consider each one separately.
2 Read again Kino's speech which begins, 'Coyotito shall go to school.' (page 19). Why is it so important to Kino that Coyotito should learn to read?

Scene 7

Questions

1 Why does Kino not greet the Doctor when he arrives? And why does he block the doorway?
2 Why does Kino finally let him treat the baby? Look at Kino's words at the very end of the scene.
3 What does the Doctor expect to happen after the baby has swallowed the white powder (page 23)?

Scene 8

Questions

1 Explain in your own words how the first merchant tries to trick Juana into buying a cagebird. How does Juana get her own back on the Merchant?
2 Juana tries to persuade Kino to throw away or destroy the pearl (page 34). Is she being silly and superstitious – or has it really brought evil to them?

Assignment

In Scene 8, the Merchants try to sell Kino things that he does not really need. In groups of two, work on a similarly improvised dialogue in which one tries to persuade the other that he or she must buy: a left-handed tin-opener, a gardening encyclopaedia, a computerised electric toothbrush . . . any item of this kind that you can think of!

Scene 9

Questions

1 How can you tell from Scene 9 that selling the pearl is a very important event in Kino and Juana's life?

2 Why are the fishermen forced to sell their pearls to the buyers in the nearest small town?
3 Look carefully at what Apolonia says about the Priest and also at Juan Tomás' comments (pages 38–39). What is Juan Tomás suggesting about the Priest's motives?

Scene 10

Assignments

1 Re-read Scene 10. Imagine you are the First Buyer. Write a report to your boss in the city, explaining what went wrong with your plan and why Kino did not sell his pearl to you.
2 In pairs or groups of three, prepare to present an improvised or scripted scene in which one person brings in an object to be valued by an expert or experts. The object could be an antique, a painting, a piece of jewellery, a family heirloom etc. It does not have to be 'authentic', but it will help a great deal if your group or your teacher can provide an actual object to handle.

Before you begin, the 'owner' should decide exactly what he/she believes the object to be, how he/she came to own it, and what he/she thinks it is worth. The 'expert' or 'experts should also independently decide what it is and what it is worth.

Play the scene twice. In the first version, the experts give a genuine valuation, which may be much more or much less than the owner expected. In the second, the experts try to cheat the owner and buy the object as cheaply as possible.

How will the experts' behaviour differ? Will they be more nervous when they are cheating?

How will the owner react to their low valuation?

Scene 11

Questions

1 In what ways has Kino 'defied the whole structure, the whole way of life' (page 45)?
2 What is Kino asserting when he repeats 'I am a man!' (page 48)

Assignment

Kino is afraid of the city. (Look at his speech on pages 44–45.) Think about what it would be like for a young Mexican on his first day in a big 'foreign' city – call it Santa Rosalia. Write as if you were someone from Kino's village. You are sitting at the window of an unfamiliar room in a cheap hotel. Write down your thoughts about what you can see, and what has happened to you since you arrived.

Scene 12

Questions

1 Why does Juana hesitate before she goes to throw the pearl into the sea (page 49)?
2 Why is Kino so cruel when he strikes and kicks at Juana?
3 Why does Juana give the pearl back to Kino after the attack, when he believes he has lost it for ever?
4 Why is Kino so upset when he discovers the robbers have smashed a hole in his canoe?

Assignment

Imagine your feelings if your own house were burnt down. All your family are safe, but your rooms and possessions are lost. What do you think you would miss most, and why?

Scene 13

Assignment

Juan Tomás makes a special present to Kino of his heavy working-knife. If your brother, sister or best friend had to go away on a long journey, what could you give to him or her as a gift? It must be something that belongs to you now. It might be practical or it might have a special sentimental value. Decide what the gift is, and explain why you would choose to give it.

Scenes 14 and 15

Questions

1 What does Kino mean when he says 'perhaps it is fate' that the trackers will find the pearl (page 61)?
2 What is Juana trying to say when she replies, 'There is no fate, Kino, only you and me and Coyotito'?
3 Do you think Juana is wrong to risk her life and Coyotito's by staying with Kino instead of hiding as he suggests (page 63)? Explain the reasons for your answer.

Assignment

Imagine the Third Tracker has kept a record of the hunt for Kino – a kind of diary. Using Scenes 14 and 15 as a basis, and your own ideas, make up this diary. It will probably begin with the news that Kino has fled from the village, and the last entry could have been made just before the shooting. It might end with the words: 'Tomorrow we make the kill.'

You may wish to produce the diary as an exhibit, in a special small notebook – dog-eared and 'bloodstained'.

Scene 16

Assignment

At the end of the story there is no implication that Kino will be prosecuted or punished for the killing of the bounty-hunters. A kind of natural justice has prevailed. He has suffered enough. However, see if you can improvise, or even script a trial scene, in which Kino is defended against a charge of murder. Cases for the prosecution and the defence would need to be carefully prepared. Witnesses might be called, such as Juana, Juan Tomás and Apolonia, or the Second Tracker, who might have survived.

'The Play of the Pearl' was first produced at Kimbolton School in March 1987. The original music was composed and arranged by the school's GCSE music group: Siobhan Dean, Richard Ford and Caroline Moore. The arrangements included: flute, oboe, clarinet, piano, synthesiser, brass and percussion.

Song Of The Family (flute)

Song Of The Enemy (brass, piano, percussion)

The Song Of The Pearl (clarinet)

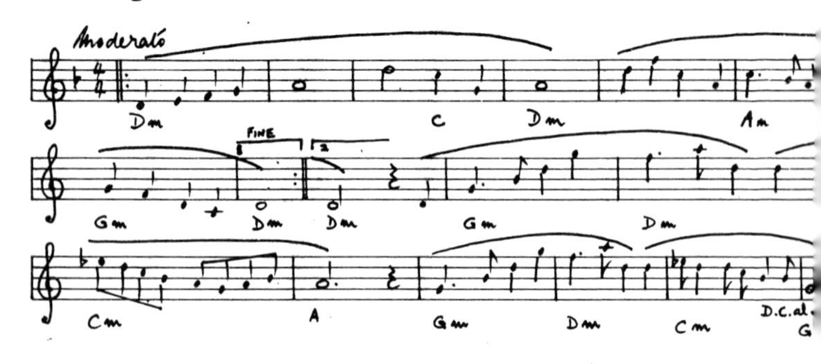